Fish Breeding and Genetics

AQUARIOLOGY

Fish
Breeding
and
Genetics

Dr. John B. Gratzek, Dr Paul V. Loiselle, and Dr. Joanne Norton.

Tetra Press

Tetra Press
Aquariology: Fish Breeding and Genetics
A Tetra Press Publication

Gratzek, Dr. John B.,
Aquariology: fish breeding and genetics; edited by Dr. John B.
Gratzek with Janice R. Matthews

L.C. Catalog card number 91-067995
ISBN number 1-56465-106-1
Tetra Press item number 16856

1. Gratzek, Dr. John B.   2. Matthews, Janice R.

Tetra would like to gratefully acknowledge the following sources
of photographs and artwork:
For the chapter "Getting Started," © Dr. John B. Gratzek; for
"Fish Genetics" © Dr. Joanne Norton. Additional illustrations
were provided by Tetra Archives, except as otherwise noted.

Printed in Hong Kong.

First edition
10 9 8 7 6 5 4 3 2 1

Production services by Martin Cook Associates, Ltd., New York

Table of Contents

Foreword

The successful keeping and reproduction of ornamental fish in a confined environment is the foundation of the tropical, goldfish, and pond fish hobby which is enjoyed by millions of people throughout the world. Information, education, and knowledge for ornamental fish keepers to be successful is an obligation for those companies engaged in providing products for home aquariums and outdoor fish ponds.

Tetra is extremely pleased to have undertaken the educational Aquariology Series of books to enhance successful ornamental fish keeping. *Fish Breeding and Genetics* is an excerpt from the Aquariology Master volume, *The Science of Fish Health Management*. For anyone who ever contemplated reproduction of ornamental fish, *Fish Breeding and Genetics* will surely be the basis for a successful endeavor.

The Aquariology Series should be the basis for any library of ornamental fish keeping books. Here is a complete listing for your reference:

The Science of Fish Health Management
Item #16855 ISBN # 1-56465-105-3

Fish Breeding and Genetics
Item #16856 ISBN # 1-56465-106-1

Fish Anatomy, Physiology, and Nutrition
Item #16857 ISBN # 1-56465-107-X

Fish Diseases and Water Chemistry
Item #16858 ISBN # 1-56465-108-8

Alan R. Mintz
General Manager
Tetra Sales (U.S.A.)

Getting Started with Aquaria

John B. Gratzek

The simplest definition of an aquarium is a container capable of holding water in which fish and other aquatic organisms can live over a long period of time. Aquariology is the study of keeping fish in aquaria. It explores the reasons for keeping fish and requires a knowledge of the biological characteristics of fish, as well as of such aspects of their husbandry as feeding and nutrition, reproduction, water quality management, sources and control of stress, and disease control.

This book is written with the hope that it will provide both basic knowledge for the beginning aquarist and more specific information for advanced aquarists, producers of ornamental fish, and those wishing to keep fish as laboratory research subjects.

Choosing Appropriate Equipment

Selecting the aquarium: Obvious considerations will determine the size of the aquarium. Available space in a particular room, the size and type of fish you wish to keep, and the cost are factors which will influence your decision. In general, larger aquaria for a given number of fish will result in fewer problems than smaller aquaria with the same amount of fish. Pollutants accumulate more slowly in a larger tank, increasing the interval between required water changes. A larger aquarium also has the advantage of flexibility—providing space for several species of smaller fish or one or two very large fish. Additionally, a larger aquarium will provide the space for planting an interesting variety of living plants.

For the beginning aquarist, it is recommended that the aquarium be no smaller than 10 gallons (38 liters) and preferably larger. A 30-gallon (114-liter) aquarium would be an ideal size for the novice. If lightly stocked, a tank of this size provides sufficient volume of water to dilute out accumulated fish wastes. At the same time, it affords ample room for fish growth and addition of new residents. For breeding purposes, a larger aquarium will provide space for particularly territorial fish as well as escape room for small fish.

Wholesalers in the pet-fish trade prefer to use aquaria between 25 and 30 gallons (95 to 114 liters) in size. To facilitate netting fish, as well as cleaning, tank height is minimized. Retailers usually employ a series of 10- to 15-gallon (38- to 57-liter) aquaria to display freshwater fish; larger aquaria house saltwater fish and the larger freshwater species.

Aquaria are sold in many shapes, from rectangular to hexagonal or cylindrical. If due attention is paid to water quality, fish will do fine in any of them. Very deep aquaria may be difficult to clean; additionally, plants may not do well in very deep aquaria because of poor light penetration to the aquarium bottom.

A sturdy stand must be selected and carefully balanced to prevent the weight from shifting once the aquarium is filled with water.

It is a good idea to clean a new aquarium to remove fingerprints and to make its glass surfaces as clear as possible before filling it with water. A small amount of dishwashing detergent dissolved in lukewarm water is perfectly acceptable for cleaning aquarium glass, provided that the aquarium is *thoroughly* rinsed with warm water afterward to remove all traces of cleanser. Scale which has collected at the water line of used aquaria can be removed with commercially available preparations designed for the removal of lime deposits. Weak acid solutions such as vinegar may also be used to remove lime deposits. Some soaking time is necessary for removal of scale regardless of what preparation is used. An alternative method is to scrape scale away with a razor blade.

Supporting the aquarium: The stated capacity of an aquarium is somewhat more than the actual volume. For instance, a standard 10-gallon (38-liter) aquarium with inside measurements of 19.25 inches (38.9 centimeters) long, 10 inches (25.4 centimeters) deep, and 11 inches (27.9 centimeters) wide will hold about 9.16 gallons (34.7 liters). Addition of gravel, rocks, or inside filters will further reduce the water volume.

One gallon of water weighs 8.34 pounds; consequently the water in a "10-gallon" aquarium—about 9.16 gallons—would weigh about 76 pounds. (The water in a "38-liter" aquarium would weigh about 35 kilograms.) Gravel adds still more

weight. If a filled aquarium is either moved or placed on a stand which is not level, the resulting twisting stress on the glass is likely to result in breakage and leaks.

Aquarium stands constructed from metal or wood are available in a wide range of styles. Stands which include a cabinet below the aquarium have the advantage of hiding equipment such as air pumps and canister filters, and can be used for storage. For research purposes where many tanks are used, double-tiered racks constructed of 2-by-4-inch lumber (standard construction studs) bolted together can be easily constructed. A rack need not have a complete solid surface to support the aquaria; placing either end of the aquaria on a 2-by-2 or 2-by-4-inch board is adequate. Racks can be built so that the long axes of the aquaria are side by side. This configuration allows an investigator to utilize space more efficiently.

Providing cover and lighting: Most aquaria are manufactured so that various types of covers or hoods fit them snugly. If a cover is not used, evaporation can be a problem. As water evaporates, the concentration of dissolved minerals and organics (uneaten food, plant detritus, fish wastes, etc.) will tend to rise. A cover will keep the air directly over the water closer to the temperature of the water, minimizing heat loss and maximizing the efficiency of the heater. The cover also prevents fish from jumping out of the aquarium, an otherwise very frequent occurrence.

Most aquarium hoods have spaces provided for the installation of artificial lighting. Either ex-

For research purposes, an arrangement such as this one at the University of Georgia's College of Veterinary Medicine works well.

There are many lighting, filtration, and heating systems available on the market. Fluorescent light fixtures are common and varied.

clusively incandescent or fluorescent illumination can be used. In some specially designed units, a combination of both types is provided. Incandescent fixtures are less expensive than fluorescent ones, but incandescent bulbs will use more electricity and will give off more heat than fluorescent bulbs, which burn "cooler" and will not substantially affect the water temperature. Another distinct advantage of fluorescent lights is that they can be purchased in sizes which cover the entire length of the aquarium and consequently provide an even distribution of light for plant growth.

The aquarist has a wide choice of types of fluorescent bulbs which emit various spectra of light waves, some of which will stimulate plant life, including algae. If living plants are not used in the aquarium, bulbs are available which are more suitable for highlighting the coloration of a tank's fish than for stimulating plant growth. Full-spectrum bulbs for plant growth are available under a variety of trade names. The wattage required for optimal plant growth depends on the size of the

aquarium. In general, 1.5 watts per gallon of water is adequate. For example, a 30-gallon (114-liter) aquarium would require a single 40-watt tube or a pair of 20-watt tubes. The performance of fluorescent tubes will degrade over time. Their replacement as often as every six months is recommended by some experts to assure optimal conditions for plant growth.

For research purposes, individual aquarium lighting is not required unless the experimental protocol requires a definite photoperiod. Generally, outside rooms with windows will provide enough natural light to facilitate observing fish. In rooms where natural light is unavailable, establishing a photoperiod of between eight and twelve hours using normal room lighting is advisable.

Buying a heater: A desired water temperature can be easily maintained by using a thermostatically controlled immersible water heater. Without heaters, water temperature will fluctuate with room temperature.

Cold-water fish such as goldfish prosper over a wide temperature range. For example, goldfish will overwinter in iced-over backyard ponds. Most species of tropical freshwater fish as well as marine tropical fish do well at 75 degrees F (24 degrees C), but can tolerate temperatures 10 degrees F (6 degrees C) above or below that optimum at which the metabolic processes of the fish are at maximum efficiency. However, as temperatures drop lower than an acceptable range for a tropical variety, there is a depression of all body functions, including appetite, growth, and the immune system. Temperatures above the optimum range can cause stress by reducing the amount of available oxygen in the water, resulting in increased respiration. Increased respiratory rates can accelerate the development of disease problems relating to poor water quality or to the presence of parasites which affect gills. For special needs, where very cold water is necessary, refrigerated aquaria are available.

The wattage of a heater describes its power— the more wattage, the more heat will be delivered to the tank. Larger aquaria will require heaters of higher wattage, as will aquaria which are situated in cooler areas. As a general rule, use from 3 to 5 watts per gallon of water, depending on the room temperature. For example, if the room temperature is kept 8 to 10 degrees F (4 to 6 degrees C) lower than the desired aquarium temperature, as in a basement area, use a heater delivering at

Proper aeration of aquarium water will ensure the success of plant growth in the "natural aquarium."

least 3 watts per gallon. Buy an accurate thermometer to use when setting the heater's thermostats and for periodic checks of water temperature. Some brands of aquarium heaters have their thermostats set to regulate water at a specified temperature.

Both immersible and fully submersible heaters are available, as are low-wattage heating pads that are placed outside and under the tank being heated.

Buying an air pump: An air pump is a necessity for a modern aquarium and serves many functions. A simple diffuser stone positioned at the bottom of an aquarium serves to circulate water by the upward movement of air bubbles. As bubbles contact the surface of the water, the agitation increases the air–water interface, causing an increase in the rate of diffusion of atmospheric gases into the water and of dissolved carbon dioxide from the water. Air pumps can be used to move water through gravel beds, in conjunction with outside filters, and through cartridges containing water-softening or ammonia-removing resins. The "lifting" of water is accomplished by directing a stream of air bubbles through a tube. The upward buoyancy of the bubbles acts like a piston moving water through a tube. A variety of air pumps is available, and all generate some sound which should be evaluated prior to purchasing the pump.

Filters and filtration materials: All of the many varieties of filters available for use in aquaria can be categorized functionally as mechanical, biological, or chemical. Many combine two or more of these modalities in a single unit.

A mechanical filter functions by trapping suspended particulate matters which could include uneaten food, fish wastes, or any kind of biological or inert particles, in a filter matrix. The size of particle which a mechanical filter will remove and the time required for removal depend on the density of the filter material. Filter media include gravel, floss, foam, or inert particulate materials such as diatomaceous earth. These act as a mechanical barrier to fine suspended particles when adsorbed to a filter screen. Mechanical filters will eventually clog and their media will require cleaning or replacement. The time required for clogging is related to pore size. Filters with a pore size small enough to retain bacteria, for example, if installed in an aquarium without some sort of prefilter, would last a matter of minutes prior to clogging. In aquaria, mechanical filters are expected to remove large particles. Removal of particles as small as the free-swimming stages of most protozoan parasites by filters is possible. However, the pore size of the medium must be small enough to trap the parasites and there must be no possibility for the parasites to bypass the filter as the medium clogs. Some parasites have the ability both to swim and to change shape. This enables them to pass through filter materials, much like a water-filled balloon being forced through a small opening.

Biological filters oxidize fish waste products, primarily by changing ammonia to nitrates. The bacteria involved in this process, collectively known as nitrifiers, are common in nature and

Scanning electron micrographs (3000x) show one of the major effects of conditioning. Unconditioned gravel (top) is barren of life, but after conditioning (bottom), bacteria are visible on the gravel surface.

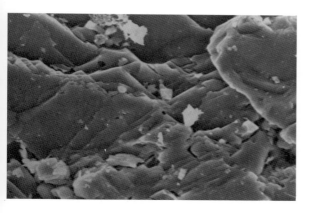

are introduced into the aquarium along with water and fish. They also are called chemo-autotrophic bacteria, because they require ammonia and nitrite ions for their growth. Bacteria of the genus *Nitrosomonas* utilize ammonia excreted by the fish as an energy source and oxidize it to nitrite ion. A second group of bacteria, belonging to the genus *Nitrobacter,* oxidizes nitrites to nitrate ion. These nitrifying bacteria initiate the conversion of nitrogenous wastes to free nitrogen. The second stage of the process, denitrification, is carried out by a different set of bacteria in the absence of oxygen. This makes it impractical to incorporate denitrification into home aquarium filter systems. Nitrifiers gradually colonize the surface of gravel, floss, foam filters, tubing, and any other solid surface, including the inner surface of the aquarium glass. (Note the scanning electron micrographs showing nitrifying bacteria on the surface of aquarium gravel.)

Chemical filtration entails passing aquarium water through some substance capable of changing the chemistry of the water. The type of change produced will depend on the substance included in the filter. Common chemically active filter media include:

1. Activated carbon. The physical structure of activated carbon includes a network of spaces responsible for adsorptive capacity. Activated carbon will adsorb a wide variety of organic substances, including color- and odor-producing substances. It effectively removes from solution dyes and chemicals used for treatment of fish disease problems, as well as dissolved heavy metals such as copper. It will remove neither ammonia nor nitrite ion from solution, nor will it soften water. Its primary use in home aquarium systems is to clarify water. Many manufacturers supply disposable inserts such as floss pads permeated with carbon particles or bags of activated carbon. Periodic replacement is necessary since temperatures required for reactivation of the carbon approach those attained in a blast furnace.

2. Ammonia-adsorbing clays. Also known as zeolites, these clays are sold in the form of chips. They require rinsing under a running tap prior to use in order to avoid clouding the aquarium's water. Many have the capacity to adsorb positively charged cations such as ammonium (NH_4^+) and can be used in filters. Since some zeolitic clays will also remove other types of cations such as calcium or magne-

sium, they also act as water softeners.

3. Ion-exchange resins. In some areas, water is "hard"; that is, it contains extremely high levels of calcium and magnesium ions. Frequently, the pH of such water is relatively high (7.8 to 9.0). Although a surprising number of fish can tolerate high levels of these minerals in water, many species will only breed under softer, more acidic water conditions. Thus many fish culturists prefer to adjust pH downward in their tanks. Doing so is difficult in the presence of calcium carbonates because the latter have a buffering effect. However, synthetic resins can be placed in a filter to soften water.

Resins which exchange sodium ions for calcium and magnesium ions are called cationic exchangers. When water is passed through this type of resin, a water test will indicate that the water has been softened. Many aquarists utilize softened water without problems for the fish. If softened water is used, the addition of a few grams of magnesium salts (Epsom salts) and calcium salts in the form of dolomitic limestone and/or oyster shell may be indicated.

The use of "mixed-bed" resins in a filter will essentially remove both cations (calcium and magnesium) and anions such as sulfates and carbonates. The resulting water is then said to be deionized. Fish cannot tolerate completely deionized water. However, partial deionization may be necessary in lowering pH in some hard-water areas.

4. Oyster shell or coral gravel. These media are usually used in a filter in areas where soft water has a tendency to become acidic abruptly. These materials contribute calcium carbonate to the

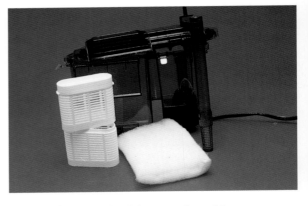

Attached to the side of the aquarium, this outside power filter has disposable inserts to facilitate the periodic cleaning that all such filters require.

water, increasing hardness and buffering capacity. In soft-water areas of the country, water in an unbuffered aquarium may decrease in pH to a point where fish are severely stressed or die.

5. Peat moss. Peat moss has been used in filters to soften water, usually for breeding purposes. It is likely that peat moss releases a hormone-stimulating substance into solution which induces spawning. Use of peat moss in a filter will impart a light brown color to water.

Choosing a filter: There is no good or bad filter. The various types available have distinct applications, depending on a variety of factors, including expense, tank size, number and/or size of fish kept in an aquarium, and whether the aquarium houses saltwater or freshwater fish. Practically every hobbyist, experienced retailer, or authority will have his or her own strong opinions on exactly what is best, but successful filtration always has both a mechanical and biological component. (Chemical filtration is required on a basis of need for special water requirements.)

These processes can be carried out using very simple or very expensive filter units—fish do not know the difference as long as the water quality is good. All filters provide for the movement of water through the filtering material, either by the air-lift principle or by electrically driven pumps. Filters may be located inside or outside of aquaria. All eventually tend to clog, resulting in reduced flow rates and inefficient filtration. All filter media, whether floss, foam pads, activated carbon, gravel, or plastic rings used for

A corner filter, which works by the air-lift principle, is appropriate for a small aquarium.

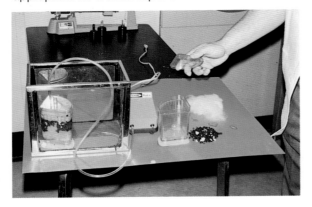

mechanical filtration, will eventually be colonized by nitrifying bacteria. The bacteria are firmly attached to the filter materials and are not removed by vigorous rinsing. Naturally, hot water, soaps, and various disinfectants will kill these bacteria and destroy the beneficial effects of biological filtration. All filters require periodic cleaning to remove debris which, although trapped within a filter matrix, is in fact still adding to the organic pollution of the aquarium water.

Since the mechanical and biological functions of filtration materials are so intertwined, it is recommended that when a filter is serviced, at least some of the media contained therein never be discarded. The easiest way to accomplish this is to include gravel, plastic, or ceramic rings in a filter along with disposable filter media such as activated carbon. Since activated carbon loses its filtering capacity after a period of time, placing it in a bag within the filter will simplify changing.

1. Corner filters. Included in many aquarium "beginner kits," an inexpensive corner box filter can be effectively utilized in smaller aquaria. Most corner filters are operated by the air-lift principle. Their filtration capacity is limited. For general filtration purposes, they function best when a small permanent sack of gravel or similar substrate is incorporated along with mechanical and chemical filter material (floss and activated carbon) to ensure that some bacteria-laden "conditioned" material remains after cleaning. Corner filters are frequently used in small aquaria for holding fish during a quarantine period or during a brief treatment period. Many aquarists interested in breeding fish use corner filters in their spawning setups.

2. Outside power filters. Most outside filters are constructed so that they can be easily hung from the rim of an aquarium. Various types of electrically driven filters are available, but most are driven by rotary impeller motors. However, an outside filter is defined only by location, and air-lift driven units are also available.

Outside power filters can be loaded with any type of filter material that meets the aquarist's needs. These generally include floss or foam pads, positioned to keep larger particulate matter from clogging activated carbon or other filter material. If gravel or other materials such as ceramic or plastic rings are included, the filter will in time develop a biological function. The waste-processing capacity of such units will be limited when

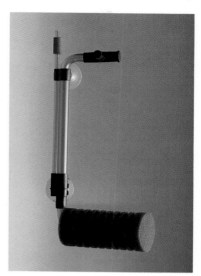

Outside power filters can be set up easily, and trapped debris rinsed periodically, with little disturbance of the enclosed environment. Foam (sponge) filters are also popular in situations where no gravel bed is to be used in the aquarium.

compared to an undergravel filter. However, aquarists wanting to avoid gravel beds for any reason will find such modified outside filters a useful alternative for use in breeding, fry rearing, or quarantine tanks.

All outside filters require periodic cleaning. Obviously, debris trapped in a filter remains in contact with the aquarium water. Depending upon the flow characteristics of the brand of outside filter being used, water may bypass the filter media as the filter clogs. This will result in less efficient filtration with little or no change in flow rate. By comparison, other filter types do not allow bypassing of water, so flow rate slows down as the filter clogs.

Cleaning outside filters is much easier if particulate media such as gravel, ceramic rings, or activated carbon are placed in separate net bags. Floss or foam pads should be cleaned whenever debris buildup is evident. Gravel bags need only

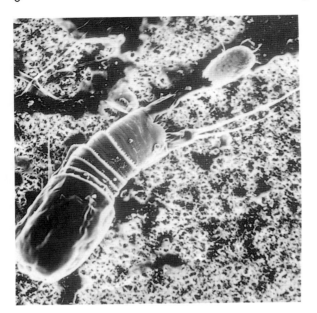

A thriving community of invertebrates will eventually develop within the filter system. This electron micrograph shows rotifers living upon a foam filter (260x).

tanks occasionally require isolation for treatment purposes, for maintaining biological filtration in quarantine tanks, and in tanks used for breeding fish.

Foam filters which have been in use for some time and which have developed a bacterial flora can be used to maintain and "seed" new aquarium systems with nitrifying bacteria. This is a simple way of avoiding the accumulation of ammonia and nitrites in freshly set-up aquaria that characterizes "new-tank syndrome."

Like all filters, foam filters will develop a thriving community of various invertebrates which provide food for fish in the aquarium. Many of these invertebrate forms are rotifers of various types. Rinsing foam filters under a stream of tepid chlorinated water will not kill the bacteria present, but may reduce the population of invertebrates temporarily. However, soaps, disinfectants, or deter-

be rinsed under tepid tap water. Activated carbon should be replaced according to the manufacturer's suggestions.

3. Foam filters. Foam pads function very efficiently as mechanical filter media. They can be used in place of floss or floss pads in any type of filter. They eventually will develop a flora of nitrifying bacteria and function well as biological filters. Foam blocks must be rinsed periodically to restore their mechanical function. The most popular types of foam filters are powered by the air-lift principle. Larger units driven by rotary-impeller power heads are also available. Foam filters certainly are less efficient than outside power filters in their mechanical action, but will ultimately develop a good biological function as well. They are useful in systems where gravel is not required or desired as a biological filter bed. They also can be used either as a tank's sole filter or as a supplement to other kinds of filters. Single pads are suitable for smaller aquaria; multiple filters can be used in larger systems. Such filters are employed with considerable success for research aquaria at the University of Georgia for a variety of experimental uses. They are especially useful as adjunct filters in recirculating systems where

Undergravel filters, the author's preference, come in many shapes and sizes. The simplest is a small flat plate (top) powered by a single air lift. For a larger aquarium, an undergravel filter with larger lift stacks powered by several air lifts (below) is ideal.

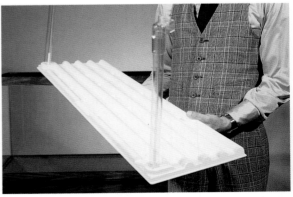

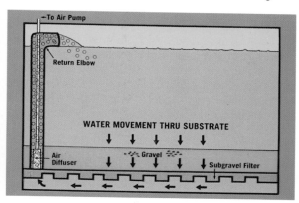

As water moves through the gravel into the undergravel filter plate, it carries oxygen to the nitrifying bacteria in the gravel. These bacteria process the fish wastes, converting ammonia to nitrites and eventually to nitrates. In this system, the entire gravel bed essentially acts as a biological filter.

gents may kill or inactivate all of the bacterial and invertebrate populations. Similarly, drying foam filters will inactivate bacteria and invertebrates. However, filters can be stored wet for several days without appreciably reducing their biological effectiveness.

4. Undergravel filters. Undergravel filters consist of a plastic plate equipped with one or more air lifts. At least 3 inches (7.6 centimeters) of washed gravel should be put over the plate. The air flow displaces water through the lift stacks, circulating water through the gravel bed. This brings both oxygen and organic wastes into contact with bacteria attached to the gravel. As long as this flow is maintained, the entire gravel bed of such a filter is biologically active. In a gravel-bottomed aquarium without water circulation, only the top centimeter or two is biologically active. Undergravel filter plates are sold in sizes adequate for the largest aquaria or for goldfish bowls. The flat plate types appear to be adequate for smaller aquaria. However, for larger aquaria, models with corrugated bottoms and larger-diameter lift stacks are likely to produce better water circulation. Undergravel units are widely employed in marine aquaria, where dolomitic limestone or coral gravel is used as the filter bed. As ammonia or nitrite poisoning is of special concern in marine tanks, the rapidity with which an undergravel filter removes these toxic substances makes it a natural choice for the marine tank.

At this writing, it appears that more and more aquarists are utilizing undergravel filtration for freshwater aquaria. Because undergravel filters act as both mechanical and biological filters, they need not be supplemented with other types of filters if (and this is an important "if"!) debris is periodically removed from the filter bed and water is changed regularly. The gravel bed is easily cleaned when water is changed by using a distended siphon tube to remove debris deep in the gravel bed. If water is changed on a regular basis, water can be kept clear without the use of activated carbon.

Of course, additional filters of any type can also be used with an undergravel filtration system. For example, an external power filter loaded with a filtering substance such as activated carbon, peat, or ammonia-adsorbing clays could be used to effect some desired change in water chemistry. Although undergravel filters are usually powered by air displacement, an alternate method is to place rotary impeller–driven units known as power heads on top of the lift stack. Placing a siphon tube from an outside power unit in a lift stack is a good way to operate an undergravel filter in conjunction with an outside power filter.

One disadvantage of undergravel filters is that some fish burrow into gravel or else actively move gravel about the bottom. This exposes the filter plate, creating breaks in the gravel which lead to a reduced water flow through the bed. This can be avoided by placing a plastic screen 3 to 4 centimeters (about 1.5 inches) below the surface of the gravel. Perhaps the chief disadvantage of undergravel filters is their immobility. There is no way to remove an undergravel filter from a tank that is being treated with therapeutic agents toxic to nitrifying bacteria, such as methylene blue, formaldehyde, or many antibiotics. Another frequently cited disadvantage is that rock formations reduce the effective surface available for water flow. From experience, I do not feel that rock formations cause sufficient blockage of the filtration surface to be of any consequence.

There is some controversy regarding the suitability of an undergravel filter for plant growth. It has been suggested that root movement which may be associated with the use of undergravel filters inhibits plant growth. However, experts in the field of hydroponics are able to grow a wide variety of plants without any root substrate and suggest that the aeration and micronutrients supplied to roots by an undergravel filter would bene-

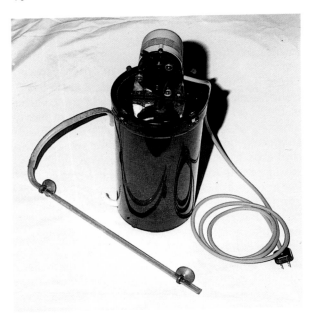

Canister filters are suitable for larger aquaria and can be loaded with a variety of filtering materials such as ceramic rings, ammonia absorbers, floss, and activated carbon.

fit the plants. Some recommend that when plants are to be used with an undergravel filter, the gravel layer should be increased to approximately 5 inches (13 centimeters). An alternative is to purchase plants which have been propagated in plant plugs containing fertilizers in a root-support growth medium. Plants can also be placed in small pots with good potting soil. It is important to place a layer of aquarium gravel over the soil in pots to stabilize it under water.

5. Canister filters. Canister filters take their name from their general shape. Their powerful motors pull water through a sealed container filled with various filter media. These filters are particularly useful in large or heavily stocked aquaria, which require a greater filtration capacity. Canister filters can be purchased in a variety of sizes. These units have two distinct advantages over other kinds of filters: they have enough volume to accommodate a series of filter substrates stacked in series, which greatly enhances their effectiveness, and they can be placed in a location remote from the aquarium. This latter feature is useful in display aquaria, for filters can be located in an adjacent work area.

Newer designs of canister filters are available in which the impeller is located at the bottom of the canister. This feature makes it very easy to prime the units and ensures that the impeller assembly never runs dry. Because of the increased size of the motor when compared to that of outside filters, some canister filters can be used in conjunction with inserts which will support a film of diatomaceous earth. These units can be used for water "polishing."

The disadvantage to canister filters is their higher cost in comparison to other types of filters. Another is that since outside canisters require tubing running to and from the aquarium, connectors must be carefully tightened and rechecked periodically lest leaks develop.

Buying gravel and ornaments: The aquaria in homes or for display purposes require a gravel base which, from an aesthetic viewpoint, mimics the bottom of a pond and provides a good base for rooting plants. For most freshwater aquaria, it is important to use quartzite or granite gravel, which will not contribute carbonate ions to water. There are advantages to using calcareous substrata in tanks housing fish that prefer hard alkaline water, such as African Rift Lake cichlids or most live-bearers.

The size range of the gravel particles should be approximately 4 to 6 millimeters (3/16th of an inch plus or minus 1/16th). The particle size is important for several reasons. If an undergravel filter plate is to be used, the spaces between gravel particles will allow free water flow and ample aeration for bacteria which will eventually colonize the surface of the gravel particles. The depth of the gravel bed will depend on whether or not an undergravel filter is used and whether live plants are desired.

Sand is not recommended as an aquarium substratum. The extremely small particle size results in packing and reduces water flow. Waste that breaks down in the resulting anaerobic conditions will generate hydrogen sulfide and other highly toxic substances. Aquatic plants also require a bed which will allow diffusion of nutrients to roots.

Marine aquaria usually are equipped with undergravel filters. Calcareous gravels, which contain carbonates, are recommended for such tanks. These include dolomitic limestone, crushed oyster shell, and coral gravel, materials containing high levels of carbonates. The slow release of carbonates in marine aquaria tends to

A multi-well tray allows many water samples to be tested at once.

buffer water towards the desired high (7.8 to 8.3) pH range.

Regardless of type, gravel intended for aquarium use requires removal of pulverized particles which can cloud tank water. Gravel should be rinsed under a tap while being stirred briskly, until the water runs clear.

Colored aquarium gravel is available. Although selection of color is largely a matter of human taste, white gravel reflects more light and may stress those species of fish which prefer dark areas in an aquarium.

Decorating an aquarium provides benefits both for the aquarist and for the fish. Many fish are territorial, and rock formations, plants, and a variety of other decorations will provide needed territorial landmarks and boundaries. Also, smaller fish may need to escape from larger species by taking refuge in small nooks provided by rock formations. A decorated tank also provides shade for those fish which prefer darker areas.

Not all objects are equally suitable for aquarium decoration. Coral, seashells, limestone, and marble will dissolve in fresh water and may increase the pH to an unacceptable level. Copper objects, galvanized metals, or steel can cause heavy metal poisoning, especially in areas where the water is soft and the pH is on the acid side of neutral. Rocks, driftwood, or gravel taken from streams or ponds should be soaked in a disinfectant such as chlorine bleach, then rinsed well, to avoid the introduction of snails and other unwanted invertebrates such as planarians and free-living nematodes.

The use of a background behind the aquarium serves to beautify the tank as well as to create the darker area preferred by certain shy species of fish. A variety of selections is available for outside use, including paints, paper with fresh- or saltwater motifs, and plastic materials constructed to create a three-dimensional illusion. Inside backgrounds constructed of a variety of waterproof inert materials are also available.

Buying water test kits: The serious aquarist should invest in test kits which will enable him or her to measure pH, hardness, ammonia, and nitrite levels. For saltwater aquaria, a hydrometer and copper test kit are also recommended. Most test kits sold for application in aquaculture are easy to use. They are based on color changes in the sample being tested, which is then compared to a color standard. Some kits are supplied with liquid reagents which over time may deteriorate. Others provide powdered reagents, which may be more stable over time. If it is necessary to test many aquaria, these kits can be used in conjunction with a tray containing many wells, each containing a water sample from a tank to be tested. This method provides a quick overview of water conditions in many aquaria.

Setting Up the Aquarium

Choosing a location: We will assume that you have purchased or built a stand which will support the weight of the fully set-up aquarium. If the tank is not level or appears to be unstable, it may be a good idea to shim the stand, or, alternatively, to fasten it to a wall to avoid accidental tipping. This can be done using an L-shaped piece of metal. The aquarium should be placed in an area where it is likely to be viewed, but not in an area where accessibility is limited. Regular maintenance will be much easier if it is possible to have working room above and behind the aquarium. Do not place the tank in direct sunlight. Otherwise, algae will rapidly accumulate and the aquarium may overheat. However, indirect light or even a short period of direct light in addition to the use of overhead lighting can be useful in stimulating plant growth. Placing aquaria close to air conditioning vents or over heat vents can complicate the task of regulating water temperature.

Equipping the interior: Once the aquarium is in the desired position, install the undergravel filter plate if this type of filter is going to be used.

Be careful not to displace gravel substrate while filling the tank with water. Rocks and plants can be more easily placed in tanks filled one-third to one-half capacity with water.

Then add washed gravel to a depth of 2 to 3 inches (about 5 to 8 centimeters) if an undergravel filter will not be used, to a depth of 3 inches (7.6 centimeters) if an undergravel filter will be used without live plants, and to a depth of 5 inches (12.7 centimeters) if such a unit will be used with plants. For better plant growth, mix a soil additive or a proprietary slow-release fertilizer with the gravel. These products are available at pet-supply outlets.

After the washed gravel is added, fill the aquarium with water to about one-third of capacity; rock formations and plants are easier to set in place if some water is present. If an undergravel filter is being used, direct water over a shallow pan to avoid displacing gravel under it. Some aquarists prefer to slope the gravel slightly toward the front of the aquarium, which they claim facilitates removing debris from the aquarium.

Construction of caves and recesses makes for more interesting viewing while providing more timid fish with shelter. Do not use any type of rock which has the potential for releasing minerals, such as limestone, marble, or clays. Rocks collected from streams can be used. However, they should be thoroughly cleaned by brushing with water, rinsed, and dried prior to placement in the aquarium.

Plants, be they living or plastic, should be positioned with the taller-growing varieties toward the back of the aquarium and in a position to hide lift stacks, siphon tubes, or heaters which you will be adding. Because living plants require a favorable water quality in addition to plant nutrients and good lighting, some experts suggest waiting to add plants until after the aquarium has been established for a period of time. Presumably, in an established aquarium, nitrification would be in place and nitrates would be available for plant nutrients.

Although fish in ponds can tolerate water temperature fluctuations, in an aquarium there is no advantage to allowing such fluctuations, which can easily be avoided by installation of a heater. Heater placement will depend on the type purchased. Totally immersible types can be positioned horizontally at the level of the gravel, a location which may enhance plant growth. Models which are not totally immersible are usually clipped to the aquarium side; they require that the aquarium water level be kept at or above the level of the thermostat to avoid overheating of the water. With either type, promoting water circulation by positioning airstones at gravel level or using power filters for circulation will help ensure uniformity of water temperature throughout the aquarium.

Water temperature should be set prior to addi-

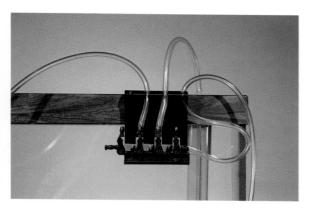

Loop the air line through notches in a tubing manifold to avoid the possibility of back-siphoning.

tion of fish to avoid any possible stress in the fish from drastic accidental changes in temperature. A good temperature for a wide variety of freshwater fish as well as plants is 75 degrees F (24 degrees C). Let the heater acclimate to the water for an hour prior to connecting the electricity. Then adjust it slowly in order to avoid possible overheating. A light will indicate whether the heating unit is on. For the first twenty-four hours, frequently check the temperature and adjust the thermostat as required to obtain the desired water temperature.

A few safety precautions should always be followed around tanks where a heater is in use. Never connect the heater unless the tube housing the heating element is immersed in water. Always disconnect the heater when changing water or lowering the tank's water level for any reason. Adjust the thermostat only when you have time to check the temperature of the water continually.

Providing aeration for the aquarium is the next matter of concern. Aquarium water is aerated by agitation of its surface by the outflow of power filters, a stream of bubbles produced by an airstone or by a stream of water splashed from the lift stacks of an undergravel filter. Gas exchange occurs at the surface of the water. Placement of an airstone toward the bottom of an aquarium will both circulate and aerate the water. Aeration of aquarium water provides oxygen required by fish, plants, and nitrifying bacteria. Aeration can always be increased by directing water flow from power filter outlets over the surface of the aquarium water. Undergravel filters have the built-in

advantage of "pulling" oxygenated water through the gravel bed.

When lines to airstones or lift stacks are attached to pumps located below the aquarium, there is a possibility of back-siphoning if the pump is accidentally disconnected or if there is a power outage. This can be avoided by positioning the air pump higher than the aquarium. If this is not possible, make sure that the air tubing to each outlet has a loop sufficiently high to avoid a siphon effect. Loops can be made by using the notches in a tubing manifold or by using plastic inserts in air tubing which prevent abrupt bending and the formation of anti-siphon loops. Check valves are also available, which can be placed in air lines to prevent back-siphoning problems.

A minimal agitation of the water surface from any type of aeration will generally result in oxygen levels of between 6 and 7 parts per million (ppm). Excessive agitation may disturb some more timid species such as discus fish. However, moderate circulation of water is tolerated by most fish and promotes plant growth.

At this point the aquarium should have gravel in place and be equipped with a filter, heater, and perhaps airstones. Fill the aquarium to the top with tap water. The air pump can be turned on immediately, but wait for a thirty- to sixty-minute period for the thermostat to adjust to ambient water temperature prior to plugging in the heater. The next step is to assure water quality that will support fish.

Dechlorinating the water: In many municipal water supplies, chlorine is added at the pumping plant to destroy bacteria pathogenic to humans. In tap water, dissolved chlorine concentrations usually measure between 0.2 ppm and 0.7 ppm, depending on the time of the year. Water for aquarium use must be chlorine-free, since even 0.2 ppm will kill fish by destroying gill tissues. Chlorine can be removed from tap water in three ways:

1. Aeration of water, resulting in diffusion of chlorine into the air. The use of a faucet-end aerator commonly found in households will aerate water and remove chlorine. Simply pouring water from one pail to another three or four times will also drive chlorine from solution. Letting tap water stand in pails for a few days also allows chlorine to dissipate gradually. This process can be speeded up by aerating the water with an air diffuser.

2. Passing water through activated carbon. Many of the faucet-end water purifiers sold to improve the taste of water are charged with activated carbon. Larger canisters available from water conditioning companies are also available for large-use situations such as would arise in a pet store.

3. Adding sodium thiosulfate to tap water immediately inactivates chlorine. Sodium thiosulfate is sold under a variety of trade names. One molecule of sodium thiosulfate will remove four molecules of chlorine. Based on this, 0.50 milliliters (10 drops) of a 1 percent solution of sodium thiosulfate would remove 0.5 ppm of chlorine from 10 gallons (38 liters) of city water. One drop per gallon of a 1 percent solution of sodium thiosulfate would provide a sufficient safety factor to avoid the consequences of fluctuations in chlorine levels.

Removing chloramines: In some municipal water plants, ammonia is added to react with chlorine to form chloramines, which then act as the disinfecting agent. The addition of sodium thiosulfate will neutralize both chlorine and chloramines. However, ammonia is released after the sodium thiosulfate combines with the chloramines, and this could be a problem to fish under conditions where there is little or no biological filtration.

In most home aquaria where biological filtration has been established, the routine use of sodium thiosulfate rids the water of chlorine; the remaining ammonia is quickly oxidized to harmless nitrates by the resident nitrifying bacteria. This assumes a very efficient biological filter and a relatively modest water change of no more than 25 percent of the tank volume at a time.

In newly established aquaria, or when most of the water has been changed at one time, sufficient nitrifying bacteria may not be present to oxidize ammonia. In these cases, sodium thiosulfate can be used in conjunction with ammonia-adsorbing media. The most readily available of these are certain clays (zeolites) sold under a variety of brand names. The ammonia-adsorbing chips should be placed in an outside or canister filter before making a water change to ensure that the ammonia released following dechloramination is quickly removed from the aquarium. An alternative method of neutralizing ammonia without using zeolites is simply to lower the pH of the water, if the tank's residents can tolerate it. At lower pH levels (6 to 7), the majority of total ammonia will be present as the nontoxic ionized form: ammonium (NH_4^+). In many areas of the country, pH can be lowered by adding buffers which are available in aquarium supply stores or by adding monobasic sodium phosphate, NaH_2PO_4.

Chloramines can also be removed from fresh water by the use of a high grade of unused activated carbon. Activated carbon which has been used may remove colors and odors, but will not remove chloramines.

In marine aquaria where pH levels are kept between 7.8 and 8.3, chloramine treatment with sodium thiosulfate would result in the generation of free ammonia. Zeolites are ineffective in removing ammonia from salt water, and lowering the pH in marine aquaria is not recommended. Before adding salt mix to tap water to make synthetic seawater, pretreat the requisite volume of tap water with sodium thiosulfate, then filter it through zeolite held in a household colander; alternatively, pass the tap water through virgin activated carbon prior to mixing it with salt.

If chloramines are present in locations where tap water is hard, with a high (7.8 to 9.0) pH, the ammonia resulting from treatment with sodium thiosulfate could injure fish if biological filtration has not been established. In such areas, pH may be difficult to adjust downward and water may have to be pretreated with sodium thiosulfate, then slowly poured through a pail containing zeolite chips before being used in the aquarium. (Holes in the bottom of the pail will facilitate this operation.) In any case, where chloramine removal is deemed necessary, treated water should be tested for total combined chlorine levels and ammonia to make sure that the treatment chosen was effective. Commercial products are also available that bind the ammonia produced by dechloramination into an organic complex that is harmless to fish. The complex is then metabolized by the biological filter.

Controlling pH: Water in various parts of the country may have different pH values, and in some cases the water may require some adjusting prior to addition of fish. Generally, fish can tolerate quite a wide pH range without problems. A pH of 6.5 to 7.8 for freshwater species is an acceptable range for maintenance of optimal health.

Purchasing and Adding Fish

Choice of fish: It has been customary to start new or unconditioned aquaria with hardy fish, supposedly more tolerant of ammonia and nitrites. There is no question that some varieties are less susceptible to nitrite intoxication than others. Our experience suggests that various species of tetras, such as the serpae tetra (*Hyphessobrycon callistus*), are less susceptible to nitrites than live-bearing fish such as swordtails, guppies, and platys. Common goldfish, zebra danios, and many barbs are also relatively hardy fish. If some form of conditioned filter—such as gravel from a conditioned aquarium or a conditioned foam filter—is added to a new aquarium, there will be less reason to fear the ammonia-nitrite problem.

A decision on what type of fish to eventually put into your aquarium is purely a matter of preference. However, you should be aware that some fish are incompatible with each other or with living plants. Different fishes also thrive in different water conditions. Some fish species may prefer brackish water. Others may do well in hard water with elevated pH, while still others may flourish in soft water with a lower pH.

A "community" tank exists when several species of fish are maintained together in an aquarium. In many cases, a few goldfish are included with species of live-bearing fish such as guppies or egg-laying species originating in South America. Such mixtures provide interesting visual variety but do not remotely reflect natural fish populations. If you are interested in goldfish, consider having an aquarium with nothing but goldfish. Alternatively, many aquarists like to create an aquarium with a few species of fish native to a particular part of the world. In many cases the schooling behavior of fish is not seen unless several fish of the same species are kept together.

How many fish in an aquarium?: In any new aquarium without an efficient biological filter system, just a few fish should be added initially. This introduction should be followed with regular water changes on a weekly basis for at least a month. As nitrifying bacteria develop in the filter material, more fish can be added.

The number of fish which an aquarium will support depends on several factors. A common rule which has been used by aquarists is that for every gallon (3.8 liters) of water, one may add 1 inch (2.5 centimeters) of length of freshwater fish or 0.5 inches (1.25 centimeters) of saltwater fish. Other aquarists suggest that the total inches or centimeters of fish which can be added should equal the number of inches or centimeters, respectively, which the aquarium measures along its long axis. A standard 10-gallon (38-liter) aquarium, for example, measures about 19 inches (48 centimeters) and thus could support nineteen 1-inch fish or twenty-four 2-centimeter fish.

It should be noted that some aquarists disregard all formulas and crowd their aquaria with fish. Their success is based on a good filtering system, a program of regular water changes, aeration, and due attention to nutrition and disease control. Nonetheless, it is generally better to have fewer fish in an aquarium to avoid deterioration of water quality and to minimize the risk of disease, which is enhanced by crowding.

Selecting healthy fish: Reputable retailers are not interested in selling an obviously sick fish, but often it is very difficult to detect fish which are carriers of a parasite and which with time will develop signs of disease. It is always prudent to select fish from aquaria where no disease has been evident over a period of time. Fish should be active, with a full underbelly. Signs of disease include clamped fins, lack of color, skin blemishes, white spots, excessive body slime, failure to eat, and inactivity. Some hobbyists will not purchase a fish (especially an expensive one) until they have observed it over a period of time in a retail shop. Particularly when evaluating marine fish, it is a good idea to ask a retailer if the animals in question have been routinely treated for parasites.

Quarantine: Quarantine refers to the isolation and observation of fish prior to introducing them into an aquarium. The objective of quarantine is to determine whether the specimen has a disease which could be transmitted to other fish. The assumption is that a serious disease is likely to develop during the isolation period. A quarantine period can vary in length, but fourteen days is common. In fish health management involving food fish, public aquaria, or fish used for research, fish may be routinely treated during the quarantine period. In cases where many fish are involved, a few fish may be killed and examined for parasites or chronic disease conditions. If disease is present, the fish are treated with a specific medication during the quarantine period. If a disease is detected which is either difficult or impossible to treat, a decision is made regarding the eventual use or disposition of the animals.

Quarantine of fish prior to their introduction into the home display aquarium is a rare, but nevertheless a recommended, practice. It is particularly advisable when adding new fish of questionable disease status to an established aquarium housing valued fish.

Adding fish to the aquarium: Although fish can live over a considerable range of water temperatures, sudden temperature changes can stress fish. It is a good practice to minimize stress by making sure that the temperature difference between the fish's transport container, usually a plastic bag, and the home aquarium is minimal (ideally less than 3 degrees F or 1.6 degrees C). In most situations, this can be done by floating the plastic transport bag in the aquarium water for ten to fifteen minutes. Keep the bag inflated during this period, since draping an uninflated bag over the side of an aquar-

Using a transport bag can allow you to introduce fish to the tank, while minimizing the shift in pH and temperature.

ium will minimize diffusion of oxygen by reducing water–air surface area.

Adding fish to the aquarium can be done in different ways, depending on the concentration of ammonia in the water of the transport container. Timely transport of a few fish in a plastic bag from a retail outlet to a home aquarium typically results in very low ammonia levels. However, on a commercial scale where hundreds of fish are transported, the ammonia levels in the transport water may be very high. Since the pH of the water in heavily packed bags is usually 6.5 to 6.8, the ammonia is in the nontoxic form. However, addition of fresh chlorinated water with a high pH (7.8 to 9.0) will serve to convert nontoxic ammonium to toxic ammonia, resulting in gill damage. This problem is particularly serious when marine fish are shipped considerable distances.

In most instances involving home aquaria, the practice of mixing aquarium water with the contents of the transport container, then adding the mixture to the aquarium, is unlikely to hurt the fish. Simply adjusting the pH of the aquarium water to approximately 6.8 to 7.0 will ensure that the ammonia levels remain low.

For wholesalers, retailers, and others who handle substantial numbers of fish crowded in bags, it is best to transfer the fish from the transport bag to the aquarium by the careful use of a net. The objective is to keep any polluted transport water and any associated disease organisms from entering the aquarium. Netted fish can be injured by contact and friction, especially if many fish are netted together. Netting injuries can be avoided by positioning a net just at the surface of a shallow container or pail filled with temperature- and pH-adjusted aquarium water. Fish in the transport bag are then "poured" into water but still contained by a net. A rapid transfer of fish into an aquarium can be effected with minimal contact of fish with the net.

Some wholesalers and brokers (trans-shippers) prefer to acclimatize fish by the slow addition of fresh water to the transport bag or to a container to which both fish and transport water have been transferred. In a matter of a few minutes, a total water change has been made and the fish can be transferred to aquaria without netting. This is an acceptable method provided that: (1) the pH of the incoming water does not differ from that of the transport water by more than 0.5 pH units in either direction and is not alkaline, (2) there is no great difference in water temperature, and (3) the water is dechlorinated.

It is always a good idea to determine the pH of the transport water, which generally will be between 6.5 and 6.8. Adjustment of aquarium water pH to between 6.8 and 7.0 prior to addition of freshwater fish is a sound and safe practice whenever the pH of the aquarium water is either much higher or much lower than the latter values.

Contrary to a widely held belief, most fish can tolerate rapid pH changes between the extremes of pH 6 and pH 9 if ammonia and other pollutants are not present. Fish in nature are often exposed to these variations without harm. Moreover, the author has experimentally shifted fish from pH 6 to pH 9 water without affecting their health. Nonetheless, overall it pays to err on the side of caution when contemplating pH changes in established aquaria. Both the direction and magnitude of pH changes must be evaluated, and this is a very complex subject. In addition, certain fish such as the neon tetra are quite intolerant of radical changes in water conditions. Thus, it is considered prudent not to alter pH by more than 0.5 units in a given twenty-four-hour period in a tank containing fish.

In the acclimation of marine fish, transport water should not be added to the aquarium, for the high pH of marine aquaria will ensure that toxic ammonia is present. After temperature equilibration, fish should be transferred to aquaria by careful netting or other appropriate methods, such as utilizing plastic containers with holes punched in the bottom as sieves. Fish can be caught easily, water allowed to drain, and the fish can be transferred quickly into the aquarium. As a rule, you can also avoid problems by refraining from adding transport water to aquaria.

Selected References

Baensch, H. 1983. *Marine Aquarists' Manual.* Tetra Press.

Hunnam, P.; Milne, A.; and Stebbing, P. 1982. *The Living Aquarium.* New York: Crescent Books.

Ladiges, W. 1983. *Coldwater Fish in the Home & Garden.* Tetra Press.

Randolph, E. 1990. *The Basic Book of Fish Keeping.* New York: Fawcett Crest.

Spotte, S. 1979. *Seawater Aquariums: The Captive Environment.* New York: Wiley-Interscience.

Vevers, G. (translator). 1973. *Dr. Sterba's Aquarium Handbook.* London: Pet Library, Ltd.

Fish Genetics

Joanne Norton

Knowledge of genetics can help the fish breeder to develop new or improved strains and to avoid some of the errors that cause inefficiency or undesirable results.

This chapter is neither a general introduction nor a review; it is intended to be somewhere in between. I have tried to present a broad overview of fish genetics to make readers aware of knowledge in many areas, some of which have not been mentioned in aquarium literature. I touch on many aspects of fish genetics, even though some of them are of no practical use to most aquarists, because anyone who is generally informed about fish genetics should be cognizant of topics such as gynogenesis and polyploidy. Many references are given to provide a good start for the reader who wants to locate literature on fish genetics.

Great advances in fish genetics have been made since Mendelian laws were found to apply to a fish, the medaka (*Oryzias latipes*), in the early 1900s. This chapter deals mainly with ornamental tropical fishes. Wohlfarth (1983), Yamazaki (1983), Purdom (1983), and Allendorf and Thorgaard (1984) reviewed the genetics of food and game fishes.

Genetics means the study of inherited variation (called polymorphism). Highly polymorphic fishes include the guppy, *Xiphophorus* species (see summary by Borowsky 1984), goldfish, betta, and some species of African cichlids. In the guppy, there are many color pattern factors, most

of which are expressed only in the male (see review by Yamamoto 1975). There are numerous species of mollies (*Poecilia*), most of which can produce fertile hybrids. Most species of *Xiphophorus* will hybridize with most of the other species in the genus, and fertile hybrids often are produced. Pigment-pattern genes occur in most species of *Xiphophorus* (Kallman and Atz 1966; Kallman 1975).

Biochemical polymorphism in fishes, which will not be included in this chapter, is discussed in Section 7 (pp. 223–339) of Schröder (1973), in Smith, Smith and Chesser (1983), and in Echelle, Wildrick and Echelle (1989).

The Genetic Material

Genetic factors, called genes, are composed of DNA (deoxyribonucleic acid), which exists in the cell in the form of a long double strand, comparable to a twisted ladder (called a double helix). Each gene has a certain sequence of the two pairs of chemical bases that connect the two strands of the ladder. Each gene makes possible the production of a certain protein, and thus genes are the carriers of genetic codes that make an organism develop and behave in specific ways. A chromosome is a long strand of DNA that consists of many genes. At certain stages of cell division, the chromosomes shorten into rods, which can be counted. Chromosome numbers vary among species of fishes. Since the reviews by Park (1974) and Ojima, Uyeno and Hayashi (1976), chromosome counts of about 1,000 teleost species (bony fishes) have been made (Yamazaki 1983).

When a cell outside the gonads divides, producing two replicas of itself, each chromosome is duplicated. Thus the chromosomes of the daughter cells are the same as the chromosomes of the cell that divided. This type of cell division is called mitosis.

Another kind of cell division occurs in the formation of the germ cells, called gametes (ova and sperm). In this division, called meiosis, the chromosome number is halved. The number of chromosomes in a gamete is called haploid, or n. When an ovum (n) and sperm (n) unite, forming a fertilized egg (zygote), the 2n, or diploid, chromosome number results. Thus in a diploid cell there are pairs of chromosomes, one chromosome of each pair having come from each parent.

A gene occurs at a certain place, called locus (plural, loci), in a chromosome. Only chromosomes with matching loci will pair and then segregate during meiosis. Such chromosomes are called homologous chromosomes.

Basics of Inheritance

Simple Mendelian inheritance: Genetic variation can result when there is a mutation, a permanent change in a gene. Genotype refers to the genetic makeup of an individual, while phenotype refers to the observable traits. The genotype of an albino molly, in which *a* is the symbol for the gene for albinism, is *aa*. The phenotype of this fish is white with pink eyes.

In the simplest example of Mendelian inheritance, a gene is expressed even when present in only a single dose. Such a gene, called a dominant gene, is denoted by a capital letter or more than one letter beginning with a capital. An example is the plumetail character in the platy, in which the central rays of the caudal fin are elongated. The gene for plumetail, *Pl,* is dominant to wild-type (Entlinger 1974). Using + (plus) for wild-type, we can write the three possible kinds of genotypes as *Pl Pl, Pl* +, and ++. A fish with a double dose of the gene for plumetail, *Pl Pl,* is homozygous for plumetail, whereas a *Pl* + fish, which has a single dose of the gene for plumetail, is

In platys, plumetail is due to a dominant gene.

heterozygous for plumetail. Wild-type is ++. When a homozygous plumetail female is crossed with a wild-type male, all of the ova will have the *Pl* gene, but none of the sperm will have this gene. All of the offspring (the F_1, or first filial generation) will have the genotype *Pl* +, and all will be plumetails. The second filial generation, or F_2, is obtained by mating F_1 individuals, brother to sister. The F_2 can be predicted by finding all of the combinations of every possible kind of ovum with every possible kind of sperm of the female and male parents, respectively. This can be done on a checkerboard, called a Punnet square. Remember that each gamete receives only one of each pair of chromosomes, and therefore only one of each pair of genes. A ratio of 3 plumetail:1 wild-type occurs in the F_2.

An F_1 cross with typical dominant and recessive alleles in platys.

		kinds of sperm	
		Pl	+
	Pl	*Pl Pl* (plumetail)	*Pl* + (plumetail)
kinds of ova			
	+	*Pl* + (plumetail)	+ + (wild-type)

An incomplete dominant gene is expressed differently when present in single and double dose. An example is the gene for dark (*D*) that is heterozygous in black lace angelfish (like a wild-

Wild-type angelfish, called silver by hobbyists, have vertical black stripes on a silver body. *Source:* Tetra Archives.

type or silver but with more black pigment) and homozygous in black angelfish (those that are black all over) (Seligmann 1958). When a black (*DD*) female is mated to a wild-type ("silver," ++) male, the ova all carry *D*, whereas the sperm are all +. This cross produces all *D*+ offspring, which are black lace. Crossing these F_1 black lace, brother to sister, is expected to produce a 1:2:1 ratio in the F_2, as follows:

An F_1 cross involving an incompletely dominant allele (*D*) in angelfish.

		kinds of sperm	
		D	+
kinds of ova	*D*	*D D* ("true" black)	*D* + (black lace)
	+	*D* + (black lace)	+ + (wild-type)

The ratio can vary from 1:2:1 because "true" blacks (*DD*) can have a high mortality rate. Therefore many spawns from black lace parents yield fewer than 25 percent blacks.

A recessive gene is expressed only when pres-

The black lace angelfish, top, is heterozygous for dark, while the black angelfish pictured above is homozygous for dark. *Source:* Tetra Archives.

ent in a double dose. A rare exception occurs when a chromosome carries a recessive gene and the other chromosome of the pair breaks and loses some genes; this deletion will be discussed in the section on chromosome aberrations. An individual that is homozygous for a recessive factor not only exhibits the trait but breeds true for that character when mated to another individual that is homozygous for the same gene. For example, albino guppies (*aa*) produce 100 percent albino offspring.

Three kinds of gold angelfish have been discovered: Naja gold, Hong Kong gold, and "new gold"

(Norton 1982b). Because "new gold," the most recent gold, is the only gold angelfish still widely available, it will be referred to as "gold" in the rest of this chapter. The gold angelfish has a recessive gene, D^g (Norton 1982b). When a gold is mated to a wild-type, ++, all of the F1 offspring have wild-type phenotype but are heterozygous for gold ($+D^g$). Mating F1 individuals, brother to sister, produces an F2 in the ratio of 3 wild-type : 1 gold.

An F₁ cross of phenotypically black (wild-type) angelfish carrying a recessive gold allele (D^g).

	+	D^g
+	+ + (wild-type)	+ D^g (wild-type)
D^g	+ D^g (wild-type)	D^g D^g (gold)

A backcross involves mating an F1 fish to the parent that is homozygous for the recessive gene. In this instance, the backcross would be F1 ($+D^g$) mated to gold (D^gD^g):

A backcross of an F₁ to the parent homozygous for the recessive gene, hence D^gD^g, in gold angelfish.

	+	D^g
Dg	+ D^g (wild-type)	D^g D^g (gold)

The advantage of a backcross, which produces offspring in a 1:1 ratio, is that it supplies a greater proportion of the homozygous recessive genotype than is obtained by mating F1 with F1.

Four recessive genes affect background body color in guppies. The gold guppy, described by Haskins and Druzba (1938), has about half as many black pigment cells (called melanophores) as the wild-type; this allows its yellow pigment to show. Goodrich *et al.* (1944) explained the colors as due to the recessive gene for gold; they also

The angelfish in the foreground is a new gold that is heterozygous for veiltail.

explained the color for blond, in which the melanophores are smaller than in wild-type. "Cream" is homozygous for both gold and blond. Albinism in guppies is due to another recessive gene (Haskins and Haskins 1948). Yet another recessive gene results in "blue," in which there is no yellow pigment (Dzwillo 1959).

Albinism, which occurs in many fishes, is due to a recessive gene in most species, such as the albino paradise fish (*Macropodus opercularis*) (Kosswig 1935; Goodrich and Smith 1937). An exception in which albinism is not due to a recessive gene occurs in the common krib (*Pelviachromis pulcher*). Langhammer (1982) reported that albinism in this fish is due to an incomplete dominant. He stated that heterozygous fry have melanophores in the upper half of the orbit of each eye, while homozygotes lack melanophores at any age. He also noted dark spots in some fins of

This female krib (*Pelviachromis pulcher*) is heterozygous for a dominant gene for albino.

heterozygous adults. I made all of the possible kinds of crosses involving homozygotes, heterozygotes, and wild-type kribs, and concur that the gene for albino is an incomplete dominant. The homozygotes grow more slowly than wild-type or heterozygotes. Using 10x magnification, I observed a small cluster of melanophores in the upper part of the orbits of the eyes of homozygous fry. I additionally found some melanophores not only in the eye orbits and fins but also on the body of heterozygous fry. Adult heterozygotes have some melanophores on the body, resulting in a faint gray pattern on a nearly white fish. The presence of melanophores in albino kribs is similar to the situation in albino guppies, in which a few melanophores are present in the embryos (Haskins and Haskins 1948).

Two-factor inheritance: The result of a cross involving two pairs of factors, sometimes called a dihybrid cross, can be predicted in essentially the same way as for monohybrid crosses.

Taking an example in guppies, we can use the symbols *g* for gold and *b* for blond. Fish homozygous for *g* are gold, fish homozygous for *b* are blond, and fish homozygous for both *g* and *b* are cream. All others are wild-type. A 9:3:3:1 ratio occurs in the F2 when there are two pairs of factors and four phenotypes.

The scales and dermis of a wild platy (*Xiphophorus maculatus*) contain small black pigment cells, called micromelanophores, and yellow pigment cells, called xanthophores, producing an

The gold platy has fewer black pigment cells than a wild platy. *Source:* Tetra Archives.

olive-brown color. Gordon (1927) referred to the micromelanophore pigmentation as "stippled." The gold platy, which was discovered in domesticated stocks, has very few micromelanophores in the scales and dermis, so yellow pigment is not masked by black pigment cells. In addition, the gold platy has a greatly increased number of xanthophores compared with wild-type (Kallman and Brunetti 1983). Gordon (1931) found that gold is due to a single recessive gene (*st*).

In guppies, a double recessive homozygote for blue (*rr*, lacking xanthophores) and blond (*bb*, having very small micromelanophores) is called "white" (Dzwillo 1962). Crossing a blond (*bb++*) with a blue (*++rr*) guppy produces all wild-type

An F₁ dihybrid cross showing independent inheritance of two traits in guppies.

sperm of F1 male (+ *g* + *b*)

	+ +	+ *b*	*g* +	*g b*
+ +	+ + + + (wild-type)	+ + + *b* (wild-type)	+ *g* + + (wild-type)	+ *g* + *b* (wild-type)
+ *b*	+ + + *b* (wild-type)	+ + *b b* (blond)	+ *g* + *b* (wild-type)	+ *g b b* (blond)
g +	+ *g* + + (wild-type)	+ *g* + *b* (wild-type)	*g g* + + (gold)	*g g* + *b* (gold)
g b	+ *g* + *b* (wild-type)	+ *g b b* (blond)	*g g* + *b* (gold)	*g g b b* (cream)

ova of F1 female (+ *g* + *b*)

Young zebra angelfish. The small ones are homozygous for zebra. The larger ones, heterozygous for zebra, grow faster.

(+b+r) F$_1$. The 9:3:3:1 F$_2$ ratio can be figured out by using a checkerboard.

In the molly (*Poecilia sphenops*), black and various degrees of black spotting are due to two pairs of dominant factors with additive effect; in *P. latipinna,* only one pair of dominant genes is involved (Schröder 1964). In *P. sphenops,* each dose of the genes for *M* or *N* increases the amount of black pigmentation. *MMNN* individuals are solid black with a black iris at birth. Fish with any three of the dominant factors are black, with a light iris and belly at birth; at maturity, these are solid black, with a black iris. *MM++* and *++NN* fish are unspotted at birth, but strongly mottled at maturity. *M+N+* individuals are slightly mottled at birth and strongly mottled when mature. *M+++* and *++N+* fish are unspotted at birth and slightly mottled at maturity. There is no spotting in *++++* fish. Many strains of black mollies are not true breeding; some of the offspring are not solid black. If these black mollies are *P. sphenops,* perhaps they could be used to obtain true-breeding blacks by selecting breeders only from black fry that have a black iris.

There are a number of modified two-factor ratios, which occur when there are either more or fewer than the four phenotypes that make up

the typical 9:3:3:1 F2 ratio. If one of the two pairs of factors is not completely dominant, six phenotypes occur in the F2. Angelfish with the dominant zebra pattern (Norton 1982a) have three black vertical stripes on the body. There are only two black stripes on the body of the wild-type (silver) angelfish. Veil angelfish have an incomplete dominant gene that causes elongation of the caudal fin (Sterba 1959). A double dose of the gene for veiltail results in a very long tail, whereas a single dose of this gene results in a shorter veiltail. When a homozygous zebra angelfish is mated to a long-veil (homozygous for veil) silver, the F1 are all zebra short-tail veiltails. There are six phenotypes in this modified two-factor ratio:

    3 zebra, long-veil
    6 zebra, short-veil
    3 zebra, without veil
    1 silver, long-veil
    2 silver, short-veil
    1 silver, without veil

The numbers in this theoretical ratio add up to 16, just as they do in the typical 9:3:3:1 ratio. In practice, the number of fish with long veiltails usually is fewer than the predicted number due to the low viability of long-veils.

When both pairs of factors are incomplete dominants, even more phenotypes occur in the F2. Then each genotype produces a different phenotype, and the F2 ratio is 1:2:2:4:1:2:1:2:1. A black angelfish without veiltail (*DD++*) crossed

An **F2 cross involving three color patterns in convict cichlids showing the effects of masking the expression of one pair of genes to yield a modified ratio of offspring.**

	+ +	+ s	p +	p s
+ +	+ + + + (striped)	+ + + s (striped)	+ p + + (striped)	+ p + s (striped)
+ s	+ + + s (striped)	+ + s s (spotted)	+ p + s (striped)	+ p s s (spotted)
p +	+ p + + (striped)	+ p + s (striped)	p p + + (pink)	p p + s (pink)
p s	+ p + s (striped)	+ p s s (spotted)	p p + s (pink)	p p s s (pink)

with a silver with long-veil ($++VV$) would produce this ratio in the F_2 were it not for the fact that homozygous D and homozygous V can be deleterious. Therefore it is common to get fewer than the expected percentages of the genotypes that are homozygous for one or both of these genes.

A modified two-factor ratio also occurs when there are fewer than four phenotypes in the F_2. In the convict cichlid, there are three known color patterns: wild-type (with black vertical bars on the body), spotted (with black splotches on the body), and pink (with black pigment in the eye but not on the body). These patterns are produced by two pairs of factors in which both the spotted pattern and pink are recessive to wild-type (Norton 1970b). The symbol p is used for pink, s for spotted pattern, and $+$ for wild-type. A pink female ($pp++$), crossed with a spotted male ($++ss$), produces striped ($+p+s$) F_1. The F_2 are in the ratio predicted by the checkerboard.

There are only three phenotypes because all pink individuals look alike whether they have the genotype for striped or spotted pattern. Thus two classes, (genetically striped) pink and (genetically spotted) pink, are lumped into one. The ratio is 9 striped : 3 spotted : 4 pink. When the genes of one pair mask the expression of the genes of another pair, the genes causing the masking are said to be epistatic to the genes of the other pair. Because the epistatic factor in this instance is recessive to wild-type, this is an example of recessive epistasis.

Another type of modified two-factor ratio occurs when an epistatic factor is dominant to wild-type. In angelfish, marble pattern (an irregular black pig-

This marble angelfish is homozygous for marble.

ment pattern) is dominant to wild-type (Norton 1982a). Zebra also is dominant to wild-type (Norton 1982c). Crossing a homozygous marble angelfish with a homozygous zebra produces F_1 offspring with the marble pattern and only slight zebra influence in the form of blue spangles in the unpaired fins and green on the head of the adult (Norton 1982d). These F_1 fish produce an F_2 of 12 marble : 3 zebra : 1 silver. This is an example of dominant epistasis, in which marble almost completely masks the effect of zebra.

Polyfactorial inheritance: When a characteristic is affected by a number of pairs of genes, these genes are called multiple factors, and this type of inheritance is termed polyfactorial or polygenic. Polyfactorial inheritance is suspected when the F_1 is intermediate between the parents, and the F_2 covers a range of one extreme to the other, with a high percentage of individuals being intermediate and comparatively few at the extremes. It is possible, from some crosses, to get individuals that are more extreme than either parent. Sailfin mollies (*Poecilia velifera*, *P. latipinna*, and *P. petenensis*) have more dorsal fin rays than short-fin molly species. Crossing a sailfin with a short-fin molly produces F_1 offspring in which the number of dorsal fin rays is intermediate between the parents. A range of dorsal fin ray numbers appears in the F_2, with a high proportion of intermediates and few at the extremes.

Linkage: Two genes that are at different loci on

The spotted convict cichlid shown here is less common than the striped morph.

The blushing angelfish is homozygous for stripeless.

Lyretail mollies have extensions of the upper and lower caudal fin rays. *Source:* Tetra Archives.

the same chromosome are linked. During formation of the gametes, these factors do not assort at random, but tend to stay together. If the genes are close to each other, they usually stay together and are inherited as a unit. But, during meiosis, linked genes that are farther apart can be separated by a process called crossing over. This results in an exchange of homologous (sections having matching loci) parts of a pair of chromosomes. If crossing over occurs in the formation of some of the gametes, then two kinds of gametes are produced: noncrossover gametes (in which no crossover occurred) and crossover gametes (in which an exchange of genes by crossover happened). The rate of crossover between two genes is predictable once the crossover rate of the two loci is known. By finding crossover percentages of more than two loci on a chromosome, it is possible to discover the location of genes on a chromosome, a process called chromosome mapping.

In *Xiphophorus,* a number of loci involving pigment patterns are known (Kallman and Atz 1966; Kallman 1975). Anders, Anders and Klinke (1973) discussed the maps of the sex chromosomes of *X. maculatus* and *X. variatus.* More recently, starch gel electrophoretic methods were used to locate enzyme loci (Morizot, Wright and Siciliano 1977; Morizot and Siciliano 1979, 1982a, b). At least sixty polymorphic loci in *Xiphophorus* are known (Morizot and Siciliano 1982b). Chromosome mapping can be useful in studying the location of genes such as those influencing inherited development of tumors in *Xiphophorus.* Biochemical linkage studies also have been done with the guppy (Shami and Beardmore 1978) and four species of

Poeciliopsis (Leslie 1982). For a review of gene mapping in these fishes, as well as in trout, salmon, and sunfishes, see Morizot and Siciliano (1984).

Chromosome aberrations: There are several kinds of chromosome aberrations which occur during meiosis and which affect the expression of genes.

A translocation results when a segment of a chromosome breaks off and becomes attached to another chromosome, often of another pair. This changes the location of linkage groups and therefore usually is detected by genetic methods before being observed cytologically. In a reciprocal translocation, chromosomes that are not of the same pairs exchange parts.

In nondisjunction, both chromosomes of a pair go to the same cell at the reduction division of meiosis instead of separating and going to different cells.

A deletion occurs when a piece of a chromosome breaks off and is lost. When a dominant gene is lost and only its recessive allele is inherited, the individual may exhibit the recessive trait. An individual receiving both chromosomes of a pair having the same deletion usually does not live.

When a broken segment of a chromosome reattaches with its ends reversed in direction, this is an inversion, which results in a reversal of the gene locations for that segment of the chromosome. This results in a change in crossover rates of the genes on the inverted section of chromosome.

Pleiotropy: A pleiotropic gene affects more than one character. An example of pleiotropy occurs in the blushing angelfish, which not only lacks the black vertical body stripes of the wild-type angelfish but also has large body areas, including the gill covers of juvenile fish, that are dull rather than shiny because these areas have decreased numbers of iridophores, cells that reflect light (Norton 1982a). The adult blushing angelfish, like the gold angelfish, lacks red color in the iris of the eye.

Multiple alleles: There are many instances in which more than one mutation has occurred at a single locus, resulting in multiple alleles. In angelfish, the dominant genes for stripeless and zebra behave as alleles (Norton 1982c). Diagrammatically we can show the chromosomes in the three possible kinds of gametes.

Above, female calico veiltail molly; below, black veiltail molly.

wild-type   zebra   stripeless

The zygote and somatic (nonreproductive) cells ordinarily carry only two of these chromosomes, one from each parent. The possible kinds of angelfish have the chromosome combinations as shown in the chart below.

Because the genes for zebra and stripeless are alleles, a fish homozygous for zebra cannot have stripeless, and a fish homozygous for stripeless cannot have zebra. Only two of a set of alleles occur in an individual. The phenotypes of the six possible genotypes are: #1, silver; #2, stripeless; #3, zebra; #4, blushing; #5, zebra; #6, stripeless, with a few black splotches on the body. Different results of crosses are obtained when multiple alleles are involved instead of genes at different loci on the same chromosome or on different pairs of chromosomes. If stripeless and zebra were on

different pairs of chromosomes, then crossing a homozygous zebra with a blushing (homozygous stripeless) would produce offspring heterozygous for each of these factors. Crossing one of these offspring with silver (wild-type) would produce four kinds of offspring, including silver, in a 1:1:1:1 ratio. But this does not happen. When one of the offspring of a homozygous zebra and blushing is mated to a silver, the offspring are zebra and stripeless, in equal numbers, and no silver, because each of the offspring receives either zebra or stripeless from its heterozygous parent. In some instances, genes that behave as multiple alleles are discovered later, after a crossover between them occurs, to be closely linked instead. No crossover between zebra and stripeless has been reported.

In the platy (*Xiphophorus maculatus*), a series of codominant multiple alleles produce tail-spot patterns composed of micromelanophores (Gordon 1931). Eight such alleles occur in natural populations (Kallman and Atz 1966). This locus is on an autosome, not on a sex chromosome (Gordon and Fraser 1931). Later it was found that the tail-spot locus consists of at least two closely linked genes instead of one (Kallman 1975).

Penetrance: A dominant gene has complete penetrance if it is expressed in every

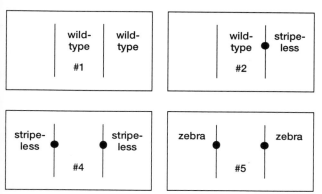

wild-type	wild-type
#1	

wild-type	stripeless
#2	

wild-type	zebra
#3	

stripeless	stripeless
#4	

zebra	zebra
#5	

zebra	stripeless
#6	

Some veiltail mollies have very wide tails, like this female from a veiltail crossed with *Poecilia mexicana*.

A *maculatus*-type platy with the twin-spot pattern at the base of the tail.

individual having that gene. If a recessive gene in the homozygous state is always expressed, then that gene has complete penetrance. When a dominant gene, or a recessive gene in double dose, is not expressed in all individuals carrying those genes, then such genes have reduced penetrance. In some instances, penetrance is higher in one sex than the other. In *Xiphophorus maculatus,* strain Jp 163, there is a gene producing spots in the dorsal fin (spotted dorsal, *Sd*); this *Sd* gene shows zero penetrance in many progenies when the Jp 163 stock is hybridized with other populations of the species (Kallman 1970b).

Expressivity: Variable expressivity occurs when a characteristic due to a particular gene differs among individuals. For example, variable expression of the plumetail character in the platy results

in variations in the length, width, and shape of the plumetail platy's caudal fin extension. The plume may be wide, long and narrow, or short and pointed.

In the molly, the lyretail mutation was discovered in a female raised by a fish breeder in Singapore (Ong 1960). Lyretail is due to a single autosomal dominant factor (Schröder 1964). Schröder, who never got 100 percent lyretails from lyretail parents, suggested that either the gene for lyretail is closely linked to a sterility factor or else homozygous lyretails are lacking in vigor and do not reach reproductive age. However, 100 percent lyretail broods have been reported (Knepper and Knepper 1963). Modifiers, genes that affect the expression of another gene, cause variation in the size and shape of the tails of lyretail

The dorsal and caudal fins of this female veiltail molly are very large.

Some platys from Lake Peten in Guatemala, as well as some swordtails, have a gene that, when coupled with the gene for twin spot, results in Guatemala crescent at the base of the tail.

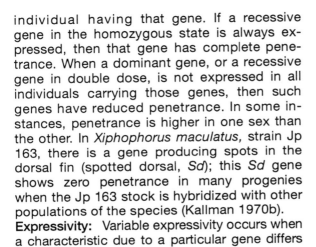

which has been derived from parts of the first three vertebrae. These small bones are called the Weberian ossicles. On each side, there is a fixed claustrum and a movable scaphium formed by the first vertebra, an intercalarium formed by the second, and a tripus formed by the third, all interconnected by ligaments. The caudal end of the tripus is attached to the gas bladder. These ossicles have been given several different names. Some of these names suggest homologies with mammalian ear ossicles, but they are not the same. Vibrations received by the bladder cause the tripus to rock and pull on the ligament, which is attached to the scaphium via the intercalarium. The scaphium pivots on the first vertebra, and as it is pulled caudally, it releases pressure on an enclosed perilymphatic sac. This sac in turn is connected to a perilymphatic duct which abuts on the sacculus of the inner ear and transmits pressure changes to the membranous labyrinth, rocking the otoliths and thereby stimulating the "hair" cells of the sensory maculae.

The girdles: The pectoral girdle anchors the pectoral fin to the skull. It consists of a posttemporal bone, a supracleithrum, and a cleithrum. Fin articulation is between the cleithrum and the basal elements of the pectoral fin.

The pelvic girdle consists of a triangular plate embedded in the ventral body musculature. Typically, it is located immediately ahead of the vent, but in many fishes the pelvic girdle is at the level of the throat beneath the pectoral fins. The girdle elements of each side are united anteriorly on the midline.

The Musculature System

The muscles of the body wall are striated and arranged as segmental myomeres along the trunk. The myosepta are attached to the vertebrae. When the muscle fibers between two myosepta contract and shorten, the body bends laterally. A wave of contractions passing down the body results in lateral undulations and forward movement.

Muscles of the fins are slips of myotomic musculature. When the fin elements are specially developed, such as to form a gonopodium for insemination, the fin muscles are hypertrophied.

In some fishes, parts of the body musculature have been modified to serve as electroplaxes to generate and store electric charges. The electric eel (*Electrophorus*) of South America can generate in excess of 350 volts; the electric catfish (*Malapterurus*) of the Nile has a lower voltage. The electric ray (*Torpedo*) of the Atlantic and Pacific coasts of North America utilizes its pectoral disc musculature to generate potent discharges that stun its prey. Lesser electric fishes include the African mormyrids and the South American gymnotids or knifefishes that communicate with each other electrically.

The striated muscles of the head serve to activate the jaws, gill arches, and opercular flaps. Six muscles (two oblique and four rectus) serve to move each eye. In addition, fish have a small muscle attached to the lens, the retractor lentis, which serves to focus an image on the retina.

The Nervous System

The brain: The brain of a fish does not fill the cranial cavity. It is surrounded by fat and can easily be exposed without damage. As the head grows, the brain increases in length. The increase may involve all regions to some extent, but the greatest lengthening is that of the olfactory tract.

Grossly recognizable parts of the brain include the olfactory bulbs, olfactory tract, and forebrain lobes of the telencephalon; the pineal body and pituitary gland of the diencephalon; the optic lobes of the mesencephalon; the cerebellum or the metencephalon; and the acoustic, vagal, and facial lobes of the myelencephalon.

The olfactory bulb of the brain remains closely attached to the base of the olfactory sac, which contains the olfactory lamellae. There is no ventricle in the olfactory bulb, nor is there a ventricle in the telencephalon. During development, the telencephalon in fishes is everted and covered by a thin, closely applied roof plate. The dorsomedial portion is considered the hippocampus; the lateral portion represents the pyriform area and amygdala. A rostral commissure connects the basal areas, while a hippocampal commissure above connects the hippocampi. The telencephalon has a central striatal area and a medial or ventromedial septal area.

The diencephalon is small in fishes. An epithalamus is represented by the pineal body, a light-receptive organ which may be accompanied by a pineal "window" of the skull for light transmission.

In the guppy, the zebrinus (*Ze*) pattern consists of two to five vertical stripes on the rear part of the body. This pattern is due to a dominant autosomal (not on a sex chromosome) gene that is expressed only in males (Winge 1927). A female can carry *Ze* and pass it on to her daughters (which will not show the pattern) and sons (which will exhibit zebrinus).

Most guppy factors are not expressed in the female, even when present, because most of the factors are expressed only under the influence of male hormones (Hildemann 1954).

Sex determination: Autosomes are chromosomes that do not carry primary sex-determining genes. Some fish, as well as some other animals (including humans), have a pair of sex chromosomes (called gonosomes), which play a major part in determining the sex of an individual. In a number of animal species, including some fishes, the sex chromosomes of a pair differ in size. However, there are some fish species in which there is genetic evidence that sex chromosomes exist but these sex chromosomes have not been observed for one of several possible reasons: (1) cytological studies have not been made, (2) interpretation of the very small fish chromosomes is difficult, or (3) there is no difference in size of the sex chromosomes of that species. Angus (1989) reviewed sex determination in poeciliid fishes. Although fish chromosomes are small and numerous, a number of karyotypes (cytological observations of chromosome complements) have been done. Yamazaki (1983) listed fish species in which sex chromosomes have been observed. Rishi (1979), who reported sex chromosomes in the giant gourami (*Colisa fasciata*), also discussed other instances in which sex chromosomes have been reported in fishes, including multiple sex chromosomes, in which an individual has more than two sex chromosomes. Multiple sex chromosomes were reported first by Uyeno and Miller (1971). Ewulonu, Haas and Turner (1985) found multiple sex chromosomes in a killifish (*Nothobranchius guentheri*) and listed the ten addi-

tional teleost species (bony fishes) in which multiple sex chromosomes occur.

In mammals and some fishes, the female has two sex chromosomes of the same kind (XX). The female is said to be homogametic. The male is called heterogametic because his sex chromosomes are different (XY). In birds and some fishes, the female is heterogametic (WY) and the male is homogametic (YY).

It was discovered many years ago that guppies have heterogametic males (Schmidt 1920; Winge 1922). However, atypical sex determination, resulting in XX males and XY females, sometimes occurs in guppies (Winge 1930, 1934; Winge and Ditlevsen 1947). Nayudu (1979) reported a brood of guppies in which a fourth were XX males. Some very old laboratory stocks of guppies, the oldest being from 1920 and 1927, produce a high percentage of females (Farr 1981). Kallman (1984) reviewed the literature on XX males and XY females as well as the literature on sex inheritance and unbalanced sex ratios in *Poeciliopsis*, limias, mollies, and *Xiphophorus helleri*.

More than two kinds of sex chromosomes occur in the genus *Xiphophorus*, in which a number of species are known to have sex chromosomes. In the 1920s and 1930s it was reported that, in domesticated stocks of *X. maculatus*, females were heterogametic and males were homogametic (Bellamy 1924, 1928; Gordon 1927; Kosswig 1934). Then Bellamy (1936) discovered homogametic females and heterogametic males in *X. variatus*. Later, Gordon (1947, 1951) found that some populations of *X. maculatus* had XX females and XY males, while other populations had WY females and YY males. Kallman (1965,

Crosses and Resulting Sex Ratios in Wild Platy (*Xiphophorus maculatus*) Populations					
Parents		**Sex Ratio of Offspring**		**Genotypes of Offspring**	
♀	♂	♀	♂	♀	♂
WY	XY	1	1	WX, WY	XY, YY
WY	YY	1	1	WY	YY
WX	XY	3	1	WX, WY, XX	XY
WX	YY	1	1	WY	XY
XX	XY	1	1	XX	XY
XX	YY	0	1	(none)	XY

1970a) found that both the X and W chromosomes occur in the same populations in 90 percent of the *X. maculatus* range. The W chromosome has not been found in *X. maculatus* from two river systems in Vera Cruz, Mexico (Kallman 1973). There are two kinds of males (XY or YY); in all except two of the natural populations investigated, there are three kinds of females: WY, WX, and XX (Kallman 1973). In the laboratory, WW females were obtained by appropriate crosses (Kallman 1968). Males and females with different sex chromosome genotypes look alike and breed at random. Gordon (1952) found that the sex ratio of the offspring depends upon the sex chromosome genotypes of the parents. For wild populations of *X. maculatus,* Kallman (1965, 1973, 1975, 1984) discussed the six possible kinds of crosses and resulting sex ratios in the offspring (using the symbols ♀ for the female and ♂ for male, see table, previous page).

Sex chromosomes were identified by the pigment-pattern genes on them (called markers) and by the sex ratios (Kallman 1965, 1970a). Atypical sex, in which the phenotype is not what is expected from the genotype, has been found for all genotypes (Kallman 1968, 1984). There are two kinds of Y chromosomes in *X. maculatus, X. milleri,* and *X. montezumae* (see discussion by Kallman 1984): Y (more common, always resulting in a male when combined with an X chromosome) and Y'(which can result in either male or female when combined with an X chromosome). Whereas Kosswig (1964) follows an old theory that sex in fishes is determined by many genes on numerous chromosomes, Kallman (1984) provided evidence that most instances of *Xiphophorus* atypical sex determination (such as an XX male) are due to the effect of a single autosomal gene on the sex-influencing gene on a sex chromosome. Avtalion and Hammerman (1978) suggested a similar mechanism of sex determination in *Serotherodon* (*Tilapia*).

Kallman (1983) listed the *Xiphophorus* species that, unlike *X. maculatus,* do not have the W chromosome. The XX female, XY male sex-determining mechanism occurs in *X. variatus, X. milleri, X. xiphidium, X. pygmaeus,* and *X. nigrensis.* The sex chromosomes of these species, and also of *X. maculatus,* are homologous (Kallman and Atz 1966). Kallman (1983) concluded that the sex chromosomes of *X. montezumae* also are homologous to the sex chromosomes of the above

six species.

Sex linkage: A gene on a sex chromosome is called sex-linked when it is linked to the primary sex-determining gene on that chromosome. Schmidt (1920) first found Y-linked inheritance, which was in the guppy. The factor Maculatus, *Ma,* which produces a black spot in the dorsal fin, was found to be inherited only by sons from their fathers. There are many color patterns in wild guppies (Haskins et al. 1961), and many of these genes have been utilized in guppy domestication (Dzwillo 1959). Yamamoto (1975) listed thirty-seven genes that are sex-linked in guppies. Some of these genes are X-linked, some are Y-linked, and all are dominant in the male. Although most are not expressed in the female, a female carrying an X-linked gene will pass this gene on to her sons and daughters. The Y chromosome in the guppy has a segment that is not homologous (does not have matching loci) with any part of the X chromosome. A gene on this nonhomologous segment of the Y is absolutely linked, as its segment does not exchange with the X chromosome by crossing over. One of these absolutely linked genes always occurs on the Y chromosome: *Ma* (Maculatus), *Pa* (Pauper), *Ir* (Iridescens), or *Ar* (Armatus).

Three genes (*Fla, Cp,* and *Nili*), each at a different locus, appeared in domesticated guppy stocks. These sex-linked genes are expressed in both sexes and may be on either the X or Y chromosome; the patterns are expressed in juveniles as well as in adults and are due mostly to melanophores. Winge and Ditlevsen (1947) stated that Flavus (*Fla*) was X-linked, and they observed no crossovers. However, Nayudu (1979) found *Fla* on both the X and Y chromosomes. Nayudu also discovered that males heterozygous for *Cp* and homozygous for *Fla* had smaller tails than males heterozygous for both genes. Dzwillo (1959) found that the factor Pigmentierte Caudalis (*Cp*) is X-linked, dominant in both sexes, and produces veiltail in males when present along with the Y-linked gene called Double Sword (*Ds*). Schröder (1969) confirmed that *Cp* is X-linked and reported a crossover rate of 8.5 percent. Nayudu's (1979) observations were the same as those of Dzwillo and Schröder except that the crossover rate was lower and the *Cp* gene was on both sex chromosomes in the same fish in some stocks.

A number of incompletely sex-linked genes (genes that can move from one sex chromosome to the other by crossover) occur in *Xiphophorus* (Gordon 1937, 1947). These genes, which produce pigment patterns, can occur on the X and Y chromosomes (Gordon 1947; Kallman 1965), but no pigment-pattern factors occur on the W chromosome in females from natural populations (Kallman 1970a). Crossover rate (less than 1 percent) between the W and Y is about the same as between the X and Y (Gordon 1937; MacIntyre 1961; Kallman 1965, 1970a). There are sex-linked genes that produce macromelanophore (large black pigment cell) patterns in *X. maculatus, X. xiphidium, X. variatus, X. milleri, X. pygmaeus,* and *X. nigrensis* (see Kallman 1983). In addition, there are sex-linked xantho-erythrophore (yellow and red) patterns in *X. maculatus* and *X. pygmaeus* (see Kallman 1983). The genes for xantho-erythrophore patterns are closely linked to the macromelanophore loci in *X. maculatus* (Kallman 1975). There are three unlinked macromelanophore loci in *X. cortezi* (Kallman 1971). A sex-linked gene that controls the age of maturation and adult size is present in *X. maculatus, X. milleri,* and *X. nigrensis* (see Kallman 1983).

Kallman (1975) reviewed the genetics of pigment-pattern genes in *X. maculatus* and discussed their enhancement or suppression when they are introduced into the genomes (gene complements) of other species of *Xiphophorus* through crosses and subsequent backcrosses. Melanomas (black cancers), which can occur when there is increased expression of a macromelanophore pattern, can result both from certain interspecific crosses, often involving macromelanophore patterns of *X. maculatus,* and

The eye of this wild platy (*Xiphophorus maculatus*) has a red iris, due to a dominant sex-linked gene.

from crosses of one population with another. Pigment-cell abnormalities in *Xiphophorus* were reviewed by Atz (1962) and Zander (1969).

In *X. maculatus,* some pigment patterns look alike but are due to different genes in different populations (Kallman 1970b). Three sex-linked patterns (spotted dorsal fin, red dorsal fin, and red anal fin) occur in populations of *X. maculatus* in the Rio Jamapa, Mexico, as well as in the Belize River, Belize. Each one of these genes is different in platys of the two river systems, and also the set of modifiers is different for each population.

Kallman (1970c) summarized the inherited patterns in *X. maculatus,* which include these sex-linked pigment genes:

1. Macromelanophore patterns. Although there are more than two dozen alleles, there are six basic patterns in addition to the wild-type (without a macromelanophore pattern): spotted dorsal fin, stripe-sided, spot-sided posteriorly only, spot-sided anteriorly only, heavily spotted all over, and black-banded.
2. A large, complex pigmentary system that includes: red dorsal fin, red anal (and pelvic) fins, red body, ruby throat, orange caudal peduncle, yellow caudal fin, and red caudal fin.
3. Deep yellow anal spot.
4. Red mouth, pigmentation of the lower jaw, expressed only in males.
5. Red iris, which is more intense in males than in females, and yellow iris.
6. Shoulder spot, a black mark with iridescent areas on both sides. This, unlike the other sex-linked genes, is recessive.

There are known at least nineteen red or yellow sex-linked patterns in *X. maculatus* (Kallman 1965, 1970a; Borowsky and Kallman 1976). Their penetrance is 100 percent in their own population, but may be as low as 30 percent when introduced into the gene pool of another population; expressivity also varies (Kallman 1975). The Jamapa population is distinct in that it tends to enhance the expression of pigment genes.

Adult size in *Xiphophorus*: Although the size of many animals is controlled by multiple factors, the adult size in some species of *Xiphophorus* is controlled by modifier genes acting along with sex-linked genes that affect the age of onset of sexual maturity. In general, early-maturing male platys (*X. maculatus*) do not grow as large as late-maturing males. The discovery that sex-

This wild swordtail (*Xiphophorus nezahualcoyotl*) was known formerly as *X. montezumae.*

linked genes control time of onset of gonad maturation in *X. maculatus* was possible because these maturation-determining genes are linked to pigment-pattern genes, which are used as markers by the geneticist. Kallman, Schreibman and Borkoski (1973), working with a Belize stock in which males are YY and females are WY, found that the Y chromosome is marked by either *Ir* (red iris) or *Br* (red body). Females are heterozygous, having either red iris or red body. Males homozygous for red body take twice as long to reach sexual maturity as males homozygous for red iris. These late-maturing males are larger than the early-maturing ones. Heterozygous males, having both red body and red iris, are intermediate in both age of maturation and adult size.

Kallman and Borkoski (1978) reported that at least five alleles of *P* control the time of onset of gonad maturation in *X. maculatus.* Range in the age of initiation of maturity in males and females was from eight to seventy-three weeks; some fish of one genotype never matured sexually. Males and females grew at the same rate until the male's growth rate decreased at the onset of sexual maturity. Males with fully developed gonopodia continued to grow, but the amount of additional growth varied with the *P* genotype. Now nine *P* alleles are known in *X. maculatus* (Kallman 1989).

The *P* locus on the Y chromosome also is present in other species of *Xiphophorus.* Adult size and the age of onset of sexual maturity in males is controlled by multiple alleles at the *P* locus on the Y chromosome in *X. milleri* (Kallman and Borowsky 1972), *X. montezumae* (Kallman 1983), and *X. nigrensis* (Kallman 1984). Kallman (1984)

discussed evidence that *X. helleri,* in which there are early- and late-maturing males, may also have sex chromosomes, even though no sex-linked trait has been found in this species.

Kallman (1983) found that, in the population of *X. montezumae* that he investigated, females are XX and males are XY. There are two kinds of Y chromosomes, one (Y-M) with a macromelanophore locus, and the other (Y-+) without a macromelanophore locus. Autosomal genes caused 9.5 percent of the XY-+ individuals to become females. The X chromosome and also the Y-+ chromosome carry a *P* allele, *a,* that causes maturation at a small size. The Y-M chromosome has an allele, *b,* which causes maturation at a larger size.

The variation in adult size of males in other species of *Xiphophorus,* as well as other poeciliids, may also be due to *P* gene polymorphism (Schreibman and Kallman 1977; Kallman 1989). In two populations of *X. nigrensis,* the slender body shape of small males differs from the deeper bodies of large males (Kallman 1983).

Hormone treatments: In some species of fish it is possible to obtain functional males by treating genetic females with a male hormone (androgen). Also, functional females have been produced by treating genetic males with a female hormone (estrogen). For example, Grobstein (1948) converted genetic female platys (*X. maculatus*) to males by treating the females with methyltestosterone (an androgen). The first hormone-induced sex reversal in both directions, male to female, and also female to male, was done in the medaka (Yamamoto 1953, 1955, 1958).

For reversal of sex differentiation in fish, it is necessary to treat them before their gonads have differentiated (Yamamoto 1953, 1962). In guppies the gonads have already differentiated in fry when they are born (Goodrich et al. 1934; Dildine 1936). By treating female guppies with methyltestosterone twenty-two days after they were mated, Dzwillo (1962) obtained some XX male offspring. These XX males, bred to untreated XX females, produced all female offspring. Takahashi (1975) also reversed the sex of guppies from female to male by treating embryos before birth.

Sex reversal from genetic female to phenotypic male has been accomplished not only in *Xiphophorus,* the medaka, and the guppy, but also in tilapia, goldfish, coho salmon, Atlantic salmon, chinook salmon, and rainbow trout. Reviews of sex control in fishes can be found in Yamamoto (1969), Schreck (1974), Donaldson and Hunter (1982), and Yamazaki (1983).

In some fishes, certain color patterns that are sex-limited to the male can be brought out in females by treating them with male hormone. Gordon (1955) gives instructions for making a solution of methyltestosterone for treating female guppies to discover their genetic makeup. Half-grown females are treated for two to four weeks by adding the hormone to the aquarium water every other day. Adult females are treated for six weeks. I tested females of the killifish, *Nothobranchius neumani,* in which there are red-tail and blue-tail males, but no such color in the females. By adding methyltestosterone to their water, I obtained females that developed either red or blue tails. However, in mangrove mollies (*Poecilia orri*), in which males have either red or yellow dorsal fin and tail color and females have colorless fins, adding methyltestosterone to their water did not cause females to develop fin color by the time their anal fins were starting to become masculinized.

Hormone treatments have been used by commercial ornamental fish producers to enhance the color of fish. Treating juveniles with methyltestosterone for three weeks changes a brown discus to a colorful "rainbow" or "blue-face" discus, and a black lace angelfish to a green angelfish (Norton 1971b). These treated fishes, imported from the Far East, were being sold at very high prices in the early 1970s. Their color fades a few months after hormone treatment is discontinued.

Another commercial use of male hormone is to change the secondary sex characters of swordtails from female to male. By treating large female swordtails with male hormone, the producer not only obtains large "males" (looking like males but not fertile) but he can also obtain equal numbers of "males" and females. It is common to see large swordtails that look like females but in which the anal fin is beginning to develop into a gonopodium. Hormone treatment of swordtails has become widely used by tropical fish producers having strains that produce small males. Female hormones also are used by some producers to increase the size of swordtails before they are treated subsequently with male hormone.

Guppy males also can be treated with female hormone to increase their size. Larr (1977) gives these instructions for treating male guppies with female hormone:

At maturity, this blushing smokey angelfish developed gold, pink, and turquoise colors.

"Dissolve one 250 mg capsule of Stilbestrol in 12 oz. of 70 percent ethyl alcohol. This in turn is diluted with distilled water to make one quart of stock solution. Add one drop of stock solution per two gallons of tank water every third day. Treatment should be started on young males at two weeks of age and be continued for about twenty to twenty-five days."

A person buying guppy breeding stock should realize that a large male may have been treated instead of having inherited large size.

There are disadvantages in using hormones to improve the appearance of fish. First, the product is misleading, not a reflection of its genotype. Second, because the true phenotype is masked, selection and culling are impaired; therefore, strain deterioration instead of improvement is likely to occur, and sex ratios may deviate greatly from 1:1. Third, there is a possibility of causing sterility in hormone-treated fish; this was reported in rainbow trout (Billard and Richard 1982).

Genetics and Breeding

Inbreeding: In a wild population of fish, deleterious recessive genes are eliminated in homozygous individuals but can be maintained for generations in heterozygous individuals. Inbreeding of domesticated fishes tends to increase the

The female lyretail sword (center) has all fins enlarged, including long extensions of the upper and lower caudal fin rays.

proportion of homozygotes, which can result in decreased vigor or viability. However, inbreeding accompanied by careful selection can result in desirable strains with no decrease in vigor and productivity. Sometimes a strain will decline in the early generations, but then improve with continued inbreeding, if selection is rigorous.

Laboratory stocks of some fish species have been maintained for many years. By the mid-1970s, stocks of *Xiphophorus* had been kept for many generations at the New York Zoological Society (Kallman 1975). *X. maculatus* had been inbred 31, 48, and 57 generations; *X. helleri,* 29 and 33 generations. Thus there are exceptions to the widely held belief that inbreeding invariably causes deterioration of fish stocks.

Mrakovcic and Haley (1979) reported inbreeding depression in the zebra danio (*Brachydanio rerio*). Kincaid (1983) reviewed the work on inbreeding of food fishes (rainbow trout, brook trout, Atlantic salmon, carp), in which inbreeding depression may result from one generation of brother–sister mating.

Selection: Some strains of fish can be improved by selecting for desirable genes and eliminating undesirable genes. Improvement may stop after one or two generations or after many generations, depending on the number of genes involved.

A gold angelfish strain can be obtained in two generations, starting with one gold individual, because gold is due to a recessive gene. Crossing a gold with a wild-type (silver) angelfish produces all wild-type offspring. Some golds, all of which are true breeding, will appear in the F2. On the other hand, the red cap (an orange area) of the

gold blushing angelfish varies from a small dot to an area reaching from the mouth to the dorsal fin. Because there are a number of intermediates in the size of this orange area, the number of genes involved must be more than two. If many genes are involved, selection for maximum red cap area would take more generations than it would if fewer genes were involved. However, once the available genes that increase the size of the red cap have been accumulated by selection, further selection cannot increase red cap size. Selection can sort out and accumulate genes, but no more. It is a common fallacy that selection, continued for enough generations, can produce unlimited increased expression of a character, in this case an all-red angelfish. Incidentally, the red cap character may not be limited to the gold blushing angelfish. Some silver angelfish, for example, have a dusky amber area at the same location, and this may be the red cap masked by black pigment. The blushing smokey male in the figure (p. 104) also has an amber area on his head.

Progeny testing: A dominant gene having 100 percent penetrance can be eliminated easily by discarding all individuals that have the character. A recessive gene, however, is not eliminated by selection, and can be carried for generations by heterozygous individuals. A recessive gene can be eliminated by progeny testing prospective breeder fish to find out whether or not they carry that gene. For example, to obtain an angelfish strain that is free of the gene for gold, nongolds can be tested by crossing them with a gold. Those nongolds that produce no gold offspring from this cross are the ones that do not carry the gene for gold, and these are the fish to save for breeders

Probably a guppy–molly hybrid, this male was infertile.

that will not produce golds.

Progeny testing also is useful in breeding fish in which the desirable modifiers are unknown in one of the parents. In the lyretail sword, modifiers affect the quality of the tail. A well-shaped tail has long extensions of equal length and is clean (without fin ray extensions) in the center part of the tail. The lyretail sword male, which has a long, malformed gonopodium, is unable to inseminate the female. Therefore, a lyretail female, which has a dominant gene for lyretail (Norton 1967b), is crossed with a nonlyretail male, either a common-fin or hi-fin. The nonlyretail male can be tested for dominant lyretail modifiers by mating him with a lyretail female having a good tail. This male should be discarded if his offspring have poor tails. Besides being influenced by modifiers of the gene for lyretail, the lyretail sword's caudal fin is affected by injury; an injured tail grows back ragged or even as a veiltail.

Sperm competition: Live-bearing females of many species store sperm and produce a number of broods from just one insemination. For example, sperm may remain viable in *Xiphophorus* females for up to ten months, resulting in successive broods (Van Oordt 1928; Kallman 1975).

Winge (1937) put a bred female guppy with a different male after she had a brood, and he found that all of the next brood were fathered by the second male. Also, in the platy (*X. maculatus*), females mated to two males on different dates produced second broods in which the sperm of the second male fertilized most of the ova (Vallowe 1953). Platy (*X. maculatus*) and swordtail (*X. helleri*) females that were artificially inseminated with mixed sperm of both species produced offspring mainly fathered by males of their own species (Clark 1950). Most species of *Xiphophorus* will cross, but *X. signum* is an exception (Rosen 1979). Kallman (personal communication to Rosen 1979) artificially inseminated *X. helleri* and *X. signum* females with mixed sperm from males of both species. No hybrids resulted; ova were fertilized only by sperm of their own species.

Sperm competition can occur not only between species but even between sperm carrying and not carrying a particular gene. In guppies, vertebral fusion produces a shortened body (palla), due to a single gene. When females were inseminated by heterozygous palla males, each succeeding brood contained a lower percentage of palla offspring (Lodi 1981); it was concluded that sperm without the palla gene were more viable than sperm having the palla gene.

Hybrids: Many fish hybrids have been recorded, both in natural populations and in cultivated fishes. Wohlfarth (1983) reviewed the literature on interspecific hybrids in Chinese carp, sunfish, catfish, and tilapia. Fish hybrids were reviewed by Schwartz (1972) and Dangel, Macy and Withler (1973). Chevassus (1983) reviewed the effects of hybridization in fish.

Hybridization has been important in the development of many aquarium strains of live-bearers. Most of the many colorful types of platys and swordtails in the trade have both platy and swordtail ancestry. Many interspecific molly crosses produce fertile hybrids.

Crossing fish of different populations, different species, or different inbred lines sometimes results in progeny that are larger and more vigorous than either parent. This effect is called hybrid vigor or heterosis. Some interspecific and intergeneric crosses produce hybrids with a growth rate intermediate between the parents. This occurs in salmonids (Suzuki and Fukuda 1972) and acipenserids (Burtzev and Serebryakova 1973).

Sterility: Many interspecific crosses of fishes produce infertile hybrids, but fertile hybrids are obtained from some crosses. From my experience, a guppy-molly hybrid is an example of an interspecific hybrid that is likely to be sterile. Kosswig (1973) discussed various causes of sterility in fishes.

In *Xiphophorus,* one type of sterility is due to lack of mobility of the sperm (Karbe 1961). In other hybrids, F1 females may be fertile, but males may be sterile because spermatogenesis (formation of sperm) is not complete (Karbe 1961). If these females are backcrossed with males of either of their parent species, some fertile males can be obtained. Repeated backcrosses can result in a greater proportion of fertile males in the progeny.

When a hybrid of *Xiphophorus maculatus* and *X. helleri* is backcrossed to *X. helleri,* some of the offspring have a sex chromosome of *X. maculatus* and some do not; those that have the *X. maculatus* chromosome can be discerned because of a pigment-pattern factor (a marker) on that chromosome. Many of those individuals having an *X. maculatus* sex chromosome are sterile. Some of these sterile fish have no germ cells in their gonads (Berg and Gordon 1953). Some of those that do have germ cells were made fertile with hormone treatment (Oztan 1963).

Chevassus (1983) reviewed the various types of sterility in food fishes.

Unisexual fishes: In some species of fish, usually all of the individuals are females. In the Amazon molly (*Poecilia formosa*), gynogenesis occurs, a situation in which the ova are activated by sperm of males of another molly species, such as *P. sphenops,* but no genetic material of the sperm is added to the ovum (Hubbs and Hubbs 1932; Turner 1982). The offspring are all females and genetically like their mother. Unisexual fishes also occur in some species of *Poeciliopsis* (Schultz 1969, 1977, 1980), goldfish (*Carassius auratus gibelio*) (reviews by Schultz 1980; Kirpichnikov 1981), and the atherinid *Mendina clark-hubbsi* (Echelle, Echelle and Crozier 1983). Chevassus (1983) discussed artificially induced gynogenesis in food fishes.

Single-sex populations: All-male populations, in which stunting of fish due to crowding is reduced, have been produced in sunfish (Childers 1967) and tilapia (Mires 1977). Many tilapia crosses have been made (Hickling 1960; Balarin and Hatton 1979; Wohlfarth and Hulata 1981). There have been attempts to find which crosses will produce all-male tilapia broods (Pruginin et al. 1975; Hulata, Wohlfarth and Rothbard 1983).

All-female and mostly-female groups of chinook salmon (*Oncorhynchus tshawytscha*) were produced by using sperm of genetic females that had been treated with male hormone to produce phenotypic males (Hunter et al. 1983). Also, when coho salmon (*O. kisutch*) ova were fertilized with sperm from sex-reversed chinook females, they produced one group of 100 percent female offspring and four groups that had over 92 percent females (Hunter et al. 1983).

Polyploidy: When a haploid (n) ovum, which contains a single complement (one of each pair) of chromosomes, unites with a haploid (n) sperm, which also contains a single complement of chromosomes, the resulting fertilized egg, and the ensuing individual, has two sets of chromosomes and is a diploid (2n). A polyploid has additional chromosomes. The role of polyploidy in fish evolution has been reviewed (Schultz 1980; Allendorf and Thorgaard 1984; Ferris 1984). A triploid (3n) has three sets of chromosomes, and a tetraploid (4n) has four sets.

Triploid hybrids of the all-female *Poecilia formosa* were produced by using males of either domesticated black mollies or *Poecilia vittata* (Rasch et al. 1965; Schultz and Kallman 1968). Triploids result when a diploid (2n) ovum unites with a haploid (n) sperm. About 1 percent of laboratory broods of *P. formosa* have one or more triploids (Schultz and Kallman 1968).

Triploid Amazon mollies also occur in the wild (Prehn and Rasch 1969). In some populations, over 90 percent of these female mollies are triploids (Rasch and Balsano 1974). Although most laboratory-produced triploids of *P. formosa* are sterile, natural triploids are fertile; they produce triploid progeny that are all females (Rasch and Balsano 1974; Strommen, Rasch and Balsano 1975).

Certain species of fishes, including salmonids and freshwater suckers, are thought to have become tetraploids during their evolution (see review by Schultz 1980). There are advantages in the artificial production of certain triploid and tetraploid fishes. For example, triploid channel catfish grow to a larger size and utilize food more efficiently compared with their diploid siblings (Wolters, Libey and Chrisman 1981). The grass carp is useful for control of aquatic vegetation, which it eats, but this fish reproduces excessively. However, triploid grass carp are sterile and their population can be limited in waters where they are introduced. Tetraploids can be useful when they can be crossed with diploids, producing triploids. Polyploids have been obtained in a number of species of fishes by physical or chemical treatment (see review by Purdom 1983). Cold-shock treatment of fertilized eggs produced triploids in channel catfish (Wolters et al. 1981, 1982), common carp (Gervai et al. 1980), and *Tilapia aurea* (Valenti 1975). Heat shock of eggs induced tetraploidy in *Tilapia aurea* (Valenti 1975) and rainbow trout (Thorgaard, Jazwin and Stier 1981; Chourrout 1982). By heat-shock treatment of channel catfish eggs, Bidwell, Chrisman and Libey (1985) obtained tetraploids, triploids, diploids, and mosaics (having tissues with mixed ploidy); the authors stated that their tetraploids may be sterile. Hydrostatic pressure is another method that has induced polyploidy in salmonids (Onozato 1983; Benfey and Sutterlin 1984; Chourrout 1984), rainbow trout (Chourrout 1984), and grass carp (Cassani and Caton 1986).

Environmental influences on phenotype: A fish's rate of growth, adult size, and color are affected not only by its genotype but also by many environmental factors, including temperature, water

Half-black angelfish are homozygous for a recessive gene. The half-black pattern can range from complete expression (top) to partial expression (bottom) to no expression at all, depending on aquarium conditions during growth of the fish.

Raised in continuous light, both this silver angelfish (top) and this black lace angelfish (bottom) failed to develop stripes on their bodies.

quality, kind of food, and frequency of feeding.

Substrate color can affect the color of some fishes. For example, red swordtails raised in a tank with a light-colored bottom are a lighter shade of red than their siblings raised in a tank with a dark bottom. Fish farmers produce the deepest red swordtails and platys in pools with dark substrate. Deep-red swordtails and platys retain their color for months after they are moved from dark- to light-colored pools or tank bottoms.

Carotenoids in the food affect red and yellow colors of many fishes. For example, the gold blushing angelfish has golden body color if it is fed newly hatched brine shrimp or frozen krill. This fish fades to near white after its diet is changed to frozen adult brine shrimp.

Breider (1935) reported that the sex ratio of the swordtail (*X. helleri*) was not affected by age of stored spermatozoa in the female, age of parents,

or a number of environmental factors, including temperature. However, there are more recent reports of environmental influence on sex ratios in fish. Temperature affects the sex ratio in *Rivulus*

When raised with fourteen hours of light each day, the zebra lace angelfish has three vertical body stripes.

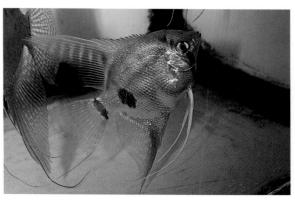

The cobra angelfish is heterozygous for dark and homozygous for zebra. If raised in continuous light, it develops spots, like this, instead of the vertical stripes it develops if raised with fourteen hours of light each day.

marmoratus (Harrington 1967, 1971) and *Mendina mendina* (Conover and Kynard 1981). Sullivan and Schultz (1986) studied the effect of temperature variation on sex ratios in two strains of *Poeciliopsis lucida*. Pregnant females were kept in water varying from 24 to 30 degrees C (75 to 86 degrees F). In one strain, the sex ratio of the offspring was 1:1 in the entire temperature range.

If a zebra lace angelfish has only one dose of the gene for zebra, instead of two as in the cobra angelfish, it develops spots and partial vertical stripes when raised in continuous light.

A silver angelfish raised with four hours of light each day (top) does not develop the two prominent body stripes of an individual raised in a fourteen-hour day; some of these short-day individuals (bottom) develop only a black spot on the body.

The other strain produced mostly males when the female parent was kept at 30 degrees C (86 degrees F) and more females than males when the female parent was held at 24 degrees C (75 degrees F). Sex ratios of some species of fish are affected by pH. In a dwarf cichlid (*Pelviachromis*), over 90 percent males develop in acid water, whereas over 90 percent females develop in neutral water, according to Heiligenberg (1965), who gave no data, however.

The fish hobby literature contains undocumented reports of poorly devised experiments on the effect of pH on the sex of fish (Ostrow 1978, 1979). Rubin (1985) tested the effect of pH on five species of dwarf cichlids (*Pelviachromis pulcher, P. subocellatus, P. taeniatus, Apistogramma borelli, A. caucatoides*) and one species of swordtail (*Xiphophorus helleri*). At low pH, a high percentage of males was produced in all six species. The low pH values ranged from 5.05 to 6.20, depending on the species. The high pH values ranged from 6.90 (*P. pulcher*) to 7.80 (*X. helleri*). At an intermediate pH (6.10), *P. pulcher* produced about equal numbers of males and females. Because similar results have not been reported for a poeciliid, repeated experiments using *Xiphophorus* (such as *X. maculatus*) of known sex chromosome genotype are needed to check Rubin's results.

Insufficient feeding can affect gene expression in some instances. An example is the half-black angelfish, which is black on the rear part of the body. Individuals that are stunted by inadequate feeding fail to develop the half-black pattern (Norton 1985b, 1989). After starting the fry on inadequate feedings, I began heavy feeding of some of these stunted fish and observed the half-black pattern beginning to develop in some of them ten days after the heavy feedings were started. No half-blacks developed in any of the stunted siblings that were kept on low rations. The half-black pattern disappeared in fry that were switched to low rations. This resulted in fish that were genetically half-blacks but looked like silvers.

Even though they appear healthy, angelfish that are genetic half-blacks will develop only a partial pattern or no half-black pattern at all if water changes are insufficient.

When the angelfish half-black pattern is either developing or decreasing in size, a smaller black area (compared with full half-black pattern) covers the tail and a rounded spot at the base of the tail. Because the half-black pattern is labile in young angelfish, a genetic half-black can have a full pattern, partial

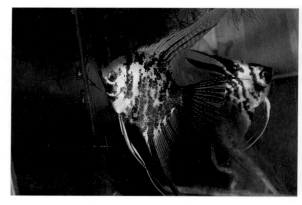

This marble angelfish is heterozygous for marble.

pattern, or no pattern. Adult half-blacks have set patterns that are not altered by environment. Adults that exhibit the half-black pattern will keep it, whereas genetic half-blacks that never developed the half-black pattern will not develop it even if their environment improves.

Some angelfish pigment patterns are affected by the length of day, called photoperiod (Norton 1982f). The marble and smokey patterns appear the same in fish raised in a fourteen-hour day or in continuous light. However, a silver angelfish raised in continuous light has no stripes. A black lace (heterozygous for dark) has black vertical body stripes if the lights are turned off at night (fourteen hours of light); raised in continuous light, the black lace is a uniform gray color, without stripes. A zebra angelfish has three black vertical body stripes if raised in a fourteen-hour day; raised in continuous light, it has only a few black

This leopard angelfish, heterozygous for smokey, homozygous for zebra, was raised in a short day of four hours of light.

This marble angelfish resulted from a marble x gold cross. It has the gene for marble on one and the gene for gold on the other of a pair of chromosomes.

This black velvet angelfish is heterozygous for dark and gold; a pair of chromosomes has the gene for dark on one and the gene for gold on the other. This angelfish also is blushing (homozygous for stripeless).

dots or splotches. A black (homozygous for dark) raised in continuous light does not have the faint vertical bars on the body that are present if the lights are off at night. A zebra lace, which is heterozygous for dark and either heterozygous or homozygous for zebra, has three black vertical stripes if raised in a fourteen-hour day. If raised in continuous light, this fish develops as a "cobra," gray with black dots, if it is homozygous for zebra

This white (gold blushing) angelfish is homozygous for both gold and stripeless. With adequate carotenoid content in its diet, the fish would be golden rather than white.

This smokey angelfish is heterozygous for smokey and also heterozygous for veiltail.

and heterozygous for dark; if it is heterozygous for zebra and also heterozygous for dark, the pattern consists of two irregular black vertical bars on a gray body (Norton 1982g).

A short day also can affect some angelfish patterns (Norton 1985a). A silver angelfish raised in a four-hour day (four hours of light, twenty hours of darkness) has only a single black stripe or spot on the body. The "leopard" angelfish, a black-dotted fish that I obtained from a pet shop, later changed to a smokey. This male, when tested by crossing him with a silver, was found to be homozygous zebra and heterozygous smokey. Crossing a homozygous zebra female with this male produced offspring that were 50 percent homozygous zebra and 50 percent genetically like the leopard parent (homozygous zebra and heterozygous smokey). Raised in a fourteen-hour day, these developed as zebras and smokeys. A

The true-breeding chocolate angelfish is homozygous for smokey.

A gold marble angelfish that is homozygous
for marble (above) has a more extensive
black pattern than one that is heterozygous
for marble (top).

second spawn, raised in continuous light, produced smokeys and fish with some black spots
but no stripes (as is known to occur in zebras
raised in continuous light). A third spawn, raised
in a four-hour day, developed as 50 percent zebra
and 50 percent leopard. A fourth spawn, raised in
an eight-hour day, also consisted of 50 percent
zebra and 50 percent leopard. Thus the leopard
angelfish is a heterozygous smokey, homozygous
zebra that is raised in a short day (Norton 1985a).

Some angelfish pigment patterns that have
been influenced by either short day or continuous
light remained unchanged a year after the fish
were transferred to a fourteen-hour day. The time

needed to set the patterns at a certain photoperiod varies with the genotype of the angelfish
(Norton 1982f).

Angelfish Breeding—Practical Application of Genetics

Angelfish usually are bred inefficiently, by making
crosses that produce two or more types of offspring even though it is possible in many instances to produce 100 percent of the desired
type. It takes much time to sort angelfish in mixed
spawns. An additional disadvantage of sorting is
that some angelfish patterns, such as black lace
and smokey (mottled on rear part of body), fade
when the fish are disturbed, making accurate
sorting difficult. Therefore, it is desirable to make
crosses that decrease or eliminate the necessity
to sort the offspring.

The inheritance of the major angelfish pigment
patterns is known (Norton 1971a, 1982a–1982g,
1983, 1985a, b, 1989). Genes responsible for angelfish pigment patterns are:

    smokey, dominant to silver (wild-type)
    stripeless, dominant to silver
    zebra, dominant to silver
    dark, dominant to silver
    marble, dominant to silver
    gold, recessive to silver
    half-black, recessive to silver

In angelfish, the half-black pattern is due to a
recessive gene (Norton 1985b, 1989), which is
expressed only when these fish are fed and maintained for rapid growth rate (see "Environmental
influences on phenotype"). Because I have seen
blushing half-black (homozygous for both stripeless and half-black), zebra half-black (heterozygous for zebra and homozygous for half-black),
zebra lace half-black (homozygous for half-black,
heterozygous for both zebra and dark), black lace
half-black (heterozygous for dark and homozygous for half-black), marble half-black (heterozygous for marble, homozygous for half-black), and
smokey half-black (heterozygous for smokey, homozygous for half-black), I deduced that the gene
for half-black is not an allele of the genes for
stripeless, zebra, dark, marble, or smokey (because only two of a set of alleles occur in an
individual).

The genes for zebra and stripeless, which be-

Crossing a silver angelfish with a gold marble produces some marbles with vertical stripes, called "barred marble." Above: a juvenile; top left: three half-grown individuals; left: an adult.

have as alleles, were discussed in the section "Multiple alleles." The genes for dark, marble, and gold act as another set of alleles (Norton 1982c). It may be discovered in the future that the genes for dark, marble, and gold are not all alleles, but that instead there exists a close linkage. It will be realized that they are not all alleles if a crossover is detected or if a fish is found to have all three of these genes.

Gold, when homozygous, prevents the expression of zebra and smokey (Norton 1982c). I do not know of any published report on the phenotype of a fish that is homozygous for both gold and half-black, although Bill Lutz (personal communication) obtained no gold half-blacks in the F_2 from a cross of gold and half-black.

Of the angelfish dominant genes, only zebra produces the same phenotype whether heterozy-

gous or homozygous. However, homozygous zebras are slower growing than heterozygous zebras (Norton 1982d). At eight weeks of age, homozygous zebras are about half as large as their heterozygous siblings. Homozygous zebras become good-sized adults and are prolific breeders

Presence of the gene for gold results in increased expression of the genes for dark and marble. A fish heterozygous for marble is not as intensely pigmented as a fish that is heterozygous for both marble and gold. An angelfish heterozygous for both dark and gold is black when adult and darker than a black lace as a juvenile (up to about quarter body size).

The true black angelfish (homozygous for dark) was the only kind of black angelfish available until the mutations to marble and gold occurred. Because some true blacks are low in vigor and not prolific breeders, they should be replaced by blacks that are heterozygous for dark. These are angelfish having the following genotypes:
1. heterozygous for both dark and marble
2. heterozygous for both dark and gold
3. heterozygous for both dark and gold, homozygous for stripeless (black velvet)

Only one strain is needed to produce black velvet angelfish, because black velvet crossed with gold blushing (white) produces 50 percent black velvet and 50 percent white offspring (Norton 1984a). The reason for this ratio is that the genes for dark and gold behave as alleles, so the offspring receive either a gene for dark or a gene for gold from the black velvet parent.

The genotypes and phenotypes of the common angelfish are shown in the table that follows.

Genotypes and phenotypes of the common angelfish.

Genotype		Phenotype
Number of doses	**Gene**	
1	smokey	smokey
2	smokey	chocolate
1	stripeless	lacks stripes (may have one or a few black splotches)
2	stripeless	blushing
1	zebra	zebra
2	zebra	slow-growing zebra
1	dark	black lace
2	dark	black
1	marble	marble
2	marble	extensively pigmented marble
1 1	dark marble	black, with faint marble pattern
2	gold	gold
1 1	smokey dark	smokey pattern on dusky background
1 2	smokey stripeless	blushing smokey
1 2	marble stripeless	blushing marble
1 1	zebra stripeless	unstriped, with some black splotches, more markings than in stripeless without zebra
1 1	dark stripeless	butterfly (gray, may have one to several black splotches on body)
1 2	dark stripeless	"blue" (blushing, gray body)
2 2	gold stripeless	white (blushing gold)

Genotypes and phenotypes of the common angelfish.

Genotype		Phenotype
Number of doses	**Gene**	
1 1 2	gold dark stripeless	black velvet
1 1	gold marble (onseparate chromosomes)	deeply pigmented marble
1 1	gold gold marble	black marbling on gold
2	gold marble	black marbling on gold, more extensive than in heterozygous gold marble
1 1 or 2	dark zebra	zebra lace
2	half-black	half-black

Below: A male red albino sailfin molly. Bottom: A wild red platy is not as intensely colored as this domestic red platy.

The situation in marble angelfish is confusing because
not every genotype produces a
different phenotype. Presence
of the gene for gold in some
marbles causes this complica-
tion. When the gene for marble
is the only mutant pigment-
pattern gene present, there are
only two types of marble angelfish: (1) heterozygous marble, having a gray and black
marbled pattern, and (2) homozygous marble, a much
darker-colored fish having very
little white. Crossing a marble
with a gold produces a third
marble phenotype in which
there is about the same percentage of white as in heterozygous marble (without gold),
but the marble pattern is jet
black instead of gray and black
(Norton 1982c); in this genotype, the genes for marble and
gold are on separate chromosomes of the same pair of
chromosomes. Another kind of
marble, called "gold marble" in
the trade, looks like the jet
black–patterned marble (which
is always heterozygous for
marble) that is obtained from
a gold and marble cross, but
the gold marble angelfish can
be either homozygous for mar-
ble or heterozygous for marble (with the gene
for gold on the other chromosome of the pair). In
general, heterozygous gold marbles have a
somewhat less extensive black pattern than
the homozygous ones, based on ten gold marble angelfish that I tested (Norton 1988). There are
now seven kinds of marble angelfish (Norton
1990a).

Crossing a gold marble with a silver (wild-
type) angelfish produces another type of marble,
which I call "barred marble." Juvenile (nickel-sized
body) barred marbles resemble silvers but have
some additional dark gray marks, most of which
are vertical. Half-grown (silver dollar–sized body)
barred marbles have irregular, black, mostly vertical markings in addition to a vertically striped

Crosses producing selected angelfish color patterns.

Desired color pattern	Conventional cross	Improved cross
black lace	black lace X black lace. Offspring: 50% black lace, 25% true black, 25% silver	silver female X true black (homozygous for dark) male. Offspring:100% black lace
marble	heterozygous marbles. Offspring: 50% heterozygous marble (fast-growing), 25% homozygous marble (slow-growing), 25% silver	silver X homozygous marble. Offspring: 100% heterozygous marble (fast-growing)
smokey	smokey X smokey. Offspring: 50% smokey, 25% chocolate, 25% silver	silver X chocolate. Offspring: 100% smokey
zebra	heterozygous zebra parents. Offspring: 50% heterozygous zebra, 25% homozygous zebra (slow-growing), 25% silver	silver X homozygous zebra. Offspring: 100% heterozygous zebra
black (heterozygous for both dark and marble)	black parents (heterozygous for dark and marble). Offspring: 50% black (heterozygous for dark and marble); 25% true black (slow-growing), 25% homozygous marble (slow-growing)	homozygous marble female X true black male. Offspring: 100% black (heterozygous for dark and marble)
black (heterozygous for both dark and gold)	black parents (heterozygous for dark and gold). Offspring: 50% black (heterozygous for dark and gold), 25% true black (homozygous for dark, low vigor), 25% gold	gold female X true black (homozygous for dark) male. Offspring: 100% black (heterozygous for dark and gold)

The molly in the foreground is the offspring of a
female sailfin molly (*Poecilia velifera*) and a
4-inch-long orange-finned *P. mexicana* male; it is
over 4 inches (12 centimeters) in length. *Collected
by:* Ross Socolof.

Calico mollies are orange and black. Top: a female; middle: a male calico sailfin; bottom: a male large-dorsal veiltail calico.

The red molly pictured (top) has a red body and red eyes. Chocolate mollies have red eyes and varying amounts of black pigment on the fins and body. Some, like this female (middle), have orange pigment; in contrast, the male (bottom) is almost solid black.

pattern like that of a silver angelfish. The adult barred marble has a faint wild-type (striped) pattern, which can fade in or out in a second, in addition to a marbled pattern that consists mostly of irregular, vertical black markings that never fade.

Conventional, inefficient crosses and more efficient methods for producing some of the types of angelfish are compared in the table.

Introgressive Hybridization

Introgressive hybridization has played an important role in the development of aquarium fishes. By this method, one or more genes from one species are added to the genetic makeup of an-

The best hi-fin swordtails are very colorful and have wide, full dorsal fins, as in this male (top) and this excellent-quality female red hi-fin lyretail (above).

other species. For example, a large dorsal fin (called sailfin) is possible to obtain in almost any color of molly that has a small dorsal fin. By introgressive hybridization, the desired one or

more genes for color are added to the sailfin molly genome by first crossing the sailfin molly with the shortfin molly having the desired color. This cross is followed by several generations of backcrossing the colorful hybrids with the sailfin. The sailfin molly (*Poecilia velifera*) does not have black spots, whereas black-spotted mollies with small dorsal fins are common in pet stores. Crossing *P. velifera* with a black-spotted shortfin molly produces offspring with intermediate-sized dorsal fins, and some of these fish have black spots. Subsequent crosses of black-spotted hybrids with *P. velifera* will increase the number of *P. velifera* genes each generation. Also, each generation will include some black-spotted individuals with larger dorsal fins than that of their black-spotted parent. The eventual result is a black-spotted fish that otherwise looks like *P. velifera*.

Gordon (1946) discussed the production of the wagtail (black-finned) pattern in swordtails by incorporation of the platy dominant gene for comet into the swordtail genetic complement. This was done by first crossing a swordtail with a comet (also called twin-bar) platy, in which the upper and lower edges of the tail are black. The addition of the swordtail gene, E, which is a modifier of comet, resulted in the wagtail pattern in the F1, but in general appearance these fish were intermediate between a platy and swordtail. A series of backcrosses to swordtails produced fish that looked like swordtails, but were wagtails because they had the comet gene from the platy and the swordtail modifier, E. Red swordtails were produced by adding a platy gene for red body to the swordtail genome by introgressive hybridization (Hubbs 1940; Gor-

The dorsal fin of this male brick-red hi-fin swordtail is wide and has an excellent shape.

This female red-velvet hi-fin swordtail has an excellent, large dorsal fin.

Many hi-fin platys have dorsal fins that are too small (top) or too narrow (above).

Branching of the dorsal fin rays results in a broad, excellent dorsal fin in this male sunset hi-fin platy (top) and this male red wag hi-fin platy (above).

don 1946). Wild red platys (*Xiphophorus maculatus*) are not as intensely red as the best domesticated red platys, in which intensified red color is due to swordtail modifiers (Gordon 1946).

Many possibilities exist for the development of new strains of mollies by introgressive hybridization. I made the first step to develop an orange–dorsal fin sailfin molly by crossing a sailfin female (*Poecilia velifera*) with a male shortfin molly (*Poecilia mexicana*) that had orange dorsal and caudal fins. The F1 had orange fins and the dorsal fin size was intermediate between the dorsal fin sizes of the parents. I obtained red mollies with medium-sized sailfin dorsals by crossing an albino sailfin molly and a red molly having a small dorsal fin. Dorsal fin size in red mollies can be increased further by additional generations of crossing those red males with the largest dorsal fins with albino females of a sailfin strain.

Developing and Improving Aquarium Fishes

New and improved strains of aquarium fishes have been produced by numerous fish breeders. The betta and fancy guppy are examples of fishes that have been improved tremendously in recent years.

I developed the orange-and-black calico molly (Norton 1981). Starting with a small male (1.5 inches or about 3.8 centimeters) that was black with some gold on the front part of the body, I made crosses with large wild mollies (*Poecilia gracilis* and *P. mexicana*); individuals with the most orange color and largest body size were saved, resulting in some 3- to 3.5-inch (7.6- to 8.9-centimeter) fish. Next, dorsal fin size was increased by crossing one of these calico females with an albino sailfin male. The second generation from this cross included some red mollies, which

This "ghost" angelfish is heterozygous for stripeless. Some individuals have one, or sometimes several, black blotches on the body.

are albino with orange or red pigment either as spots or almost solid red (Norton 1984b). Veiltail also has been added to calico mollies.

In live-bearers, it sometimes is possible to derive a strain from a single male even if he is unable to breed. A few hobbyists have used male lyretail swords, which are unable to breed, by artificial insemination, using methods similar to that of Clark (1950). In 1980, albino red mollies were imported from Singapore. No females were supplied, and all of the males had their gonopodia amputated. I squeezed sperm from one of these males and artificially inseminated an albino sailfin female. The resulting albino offspring included

some individuals with red spots. Subsequent crosses and selection led to red mollies which were larger and had improved color and dorsal fin size, compared with the imported males.

The chocolate molly is an albino (having pink eyes) with orange or red pigment in addition to varying amounts of black pigment; some individuals are entirely black, with pink eyes. I developed a strain of red mollies by first crossing a calico female, which carried albino, with a chocolate male. In later generations, albino individuals with much red and little or no black were obtained by selecting breeders with the least black pigment. Opinion varies as to whether a fish having any black pigment should be considered as an albino. For our purposes, I shall call an albino any fish having pink eyes, even though there may be black pigment on the fish. Breider (1938) reported *Xiphophorus* hybrids in which pink-eyed albino individuals were black or had black patches at birth. The black pigment later faded, then reappeared in older fish. Gordon (1950) also reported albino platy-swordtail hybrids that were pink-eyed but had black pigment at birth. The chocolate molly and the black-pigmented platy-swordtail hybrids of Breider and Gordon are examples of fish in which one or more certain genes override the effect of the gene for albino. The red coral swordtail is similar. This swordtail is a red albino with the same dominant factor that causes the black band on the body of a tuxedo swordtail. In the red coral swordtail, the red body has a wide white lateral band which develops some black pigment in many

Two sides of an unusual male angelfish discovered by Scottie Shroff in a spawn of golds. The fish was a genetic mosaic, having mixed tissue areas (some gold, others gold–dark), subsequent to a mutation early in its development. Half of its offspring inherited the gene for gold and the other half the gene for dark.

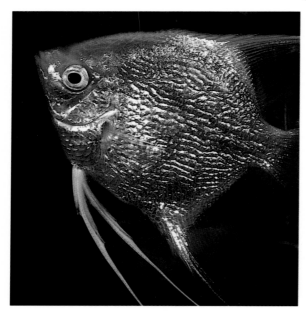

A female pearlscale angelfish.

older individuals (Norton 1969).

A mutation in an aquarium stock of swordtails resulted in a male with an enlarged dorsal fin, called "hi-fin" (Wolfsheimer 1960). Hi-fin is due to an autosomal dominant factor (Schröder 1966). The hi-fin character was transferred to platys by introgressive hybridization (Hearin 1963). Homozygous hi-fins ordinarily do not occur (Schröder 1966; Norton 1967a). A cross of a hi-fin ($H+$) with a common (++) produces 50 percent hi-fin ($H+$) and 50 percent common offspring. Two hi-fin parents produce a ratio of 2 hi-fin ($H+$):1 common (++), because HH offspring usually do not survive. I have found only one instance in which all of the offspring were hi-fins. This was a brood of about fifty platys, some of which grew slowly and did not reach reproductive age.

Good quality hi-fin swordtails are rare, and there is great variation between a poor quality hi-fin with a small, narrow, or poorly shaped dorsal fin and a good quality hi-fin. Hi-fin platys also are extremely variable. A narrow dorsal fin has unbranched anterior dorsal fin rays. A wide hi-fin dorsal fin has rays with repeated dichotomous branching. A fault that occurs in some hi-fin swordtails and platys, even if their parents do not manifest the fault, is "pinched dorsal," in which a few anterior dorsal fin rays are bent backward near the base of the fin. Evidence that pinched dorsal fin is caused by a recessive modifier of hi-fin came from three broods produced by hi-fins that did not have pinched dorsal fins: two of thirteen hi-fin platys, three of fifteen hi-fin platys, and four of fifteen hi-fin swordtails had pinched dorsal fins. Because the hi-fin dorsal fin size and shape are affected by numerous genes, it is unwise to outcross a good hi-fin strain unless the purpose is to add other characteristics. I obtained only fish with poor dorsal fins in the offspring of a good hi-fin swordtail and a low-fin swordtail.

All of the fins are enlarged in a lyretail sword. The lyretail male's gonopodium is very long, an inch (2.5 centimeters) or more, and he is unable to inseminate the female. Some aquarists have suggested cutting off most of the gonopodium to enable the male to breed. This is not effective because a male swordtail is not able to copulate without the structure, called the holdfast mechanism, at the tip of the gonopodium. Clark, Aronson and Gordon (1954) found that swordtail males were not able to inseminate females after the tips of their gonopodia were amputated. Because lyretail sword males are not able to breed, lyretail females are mated to nonlyretail males, producing 50 percent lyretail offspring. The hi-fin and lyretail characters can be combined, producing a hi-fin lyretail.

The clown angelfish is a zebra lace that develops an irregular pattern instead of the three vertical body stripes of the more common type of zebra lace.

The size and shape of the caudal fin of the veiltail molly is variable, and veiltails with large, wide tails are scarce. The objective in breeding veiltail mollies is to incorporate the veiltail modifiers that result in large tails. It is not known how many or in which wild mollies such modifiers exist. One method to try to improve veiltail mollies is to use introgressive hybridization to introduce the dominant gene for veiltail into the genomes of various species of mollies. This amounts to combing the species for the desirable modifiers of veiltail. The initial cross of a veiltail female (most veiltail males are not able to breed) with a male of a certain species should be followed by at least one backcross of an F1 veiltail female to a male of the same species as her father.

Recognizing useful genetic variations: Mutations that occur in domesticated stocks may be lost unless someone recognizes their value and works with them. In many instances it is impossible to know by the appearance of a variation whether or not it is genetic. For example, a silver angelfish raised in continuous light looks like an angelfish heterozygous for stripeless that was raised in a fourteen-hour day.

Veiltail swordtails were reported in 1970 (Norton 1970a). In swordtails, veiltail is not entirely genetic, although a veiltail is a modified lyretail. After a lyretail sword's caudal fin is cut off or injured, the tail grows back as a veiltail instead of a lyretail. The commonly encountered ragged tails of lyretail swords commercially produced in pools could be due to inherited variation of lyretail or it could be the result of injury, perhaps by trapping, netting, and sorting of these fish. I had a veiltail swordtail in which veiltails resulted from tail injury due to an infection of the caudal fins of lyretails. A veiltail swordtail female mated to a common male produced three lyretail, four veiltail, and eight common. An infection on the edge of the caudal fin was observed in a few of the fry when they were five days old; these developed veiltails. There was no tail infection in any fish that were not lyretails. One of the fry with a tail infection was found by microscopic examination to have a protozoan infection on the tail. In these swordtails, the veiltail is due to the gene for lyretail along with an inherited predisposition to tail infection.

A gold angelfish with striking black markings was found by Scottie Shroff, who gave this male to me. The parents, grandparents, and great-grandparents of this fish were golds. Crossing this unusual male with a gold female produced no

The golden color of this molly, collected by Ross Socolof in a cave in Mexico, is due to a recessive gene.

offspring like him; instead, he produced offspring like that of a black male, the type of black that is heterozygous for gold and dark. The offspring were 50 percent blacks and 50 percent golds. Backcrosses of the Shroff male to his gold daughters produced blacks and golds, but none of the golds had black markings. The Shroff male is a mosaic, which results when a mutation occurs in a cell of the embryo. In this instance, cells arising from that cell have the gene for dark along with the gene for gold; the rest of the tissues are homozygous for gold. If the gene for dark is in the reproductive tissues of the Shroff angelfish, then this male would produce two kinds of sperm, one kind with the gene for gold and the other kind with the gene for dark.

The pearlscale angelfish has raised scales in wavy rows, causing the body to glitter. This trait is

The orange color of this "peach" molly was the result of adding the genes for golden, from the golden form of the Mexican cave molly, to an albino molly.

due to a recessive gene (Norton 1990b) that has been added to other colors of angelfish besides gold.

"Clown" is an inherited variation of zebra lace in angelfish (Norton 1983). The zebra lace has three vertical black stripes on the body, while clown is a zebra lace with irregular black markings. At least some clown parents produce offspring in which all of the zebra lace are the clown variation.

The utilization of desirable gene modifiers was discussed earlier in the chapter. There are genes in wild fish populations which could be useful in ornamental fish breeding. In addition, wild populations may exhibit useful genetic variations that might be added to domesticated fishes. The golden cave molly is an example of a wild fish that has a useful gene for molly breeding. Ross Socolof collected some mollies from a cave in Mexico. He sent four of these, three gray and one golden, to me; I found that the golden color in these mollies is due to a single recessive gene. Combining golden with albino resulted in an attractive pastel orange color (Norton 1986) called peach.

Mutations are important in adding to the variety of aquarium fishes. If a fish with a desirable new character is discovered, it should be saved, and an attempt should be made to increase the stock and find out whether the variation is inherited. One of the most exciting aspects of fish-keeping is the discovery and propagation of a valuable new fish.

References

Allendorf, F. W., and Thorgaard, G. H. 1984. Tetraploidy and the evolution of salmonid fishes. In *Evolutionary Genetics of Fishes,* ed. B. J. Turner, 1–53. New York: Plenum Press.

Anders, A.; Anders, F.; and Klinke, K. 1973. Regulation of gene expression in the Gordon-Kosswig melanoma system. II. The arrangement of chromatophore determining loci and regulating elements in the sex chromosomes of Xiphophorin fish, *Platypoecilus maculatus* and *Platypoecilus variatus.* In *Genetics and Mutagenesis of Fish,* ed. J. H. Schröder, 53–63. New York: Springer-Verlag.

Angus, R. A. 1989. A genetic overview of poeciliid fishes. In *Ecology and Evolution of Livebearing Fishes (Poeciliidae),* eds. G. H. Meffe and F. F. Snelson, Jr., 51–68. Englewood Cliffs, N.J.: Prentice-Hall.

Atz, J. W. 1962. Effects of hybridization on pigmentation in fishes of the genus *Xiphophorus. Zoologica* (N.Y.) 47:153–81.

Avtalion, R. R., and Hammerman, I. S. 1978. Sex determination in *Sarotherodon* (Tilapia). I. Introduction to a theory of autosomal influence. *Bamidgeh* 30:110–15.

Balarin, J. D., and Hatton, J. P. 1979. *Tilapia—A Guide to Their Biology and Culture in Africa.* Stirling, U.K.: University of Stirling.

Bellamy, A. W. 1924. Bionomic studies on certain teleosts (Poeciliinae). I. Statement of problems, description of material, and general notes on life histories and breeding behavior under laboratory conditions. *Genetics* 9:513–29.

———. 1928. Bionomic studies on certain teleosts (Poeciliinae). II. Color pattern inheritance and sex in *Platypoecilus maculatus* (Gunth.). *Genetics* 13:226–32.

———. 1936. Inter-specific hybrids in *Platypoecilus:* one species ZZ-WZ; the other XY-XX. *Proc. Nat. Acad. Sci.* 22:531–35.

Benfey, T. J., and Sutterlin, A. M. 1984. Triploidy induced by heat shock and hydrostatic pressure in landlocked Atlantic salmon (*Salmo salar* L.). *Aquaculture* 36:359–67.

Berg, O., and Gordon, M. 1953. Relationship of atypical pigment cell growth to gonadal development in hybrid fishes. In *Pigment Cell Growth,* ed. M. Gordon, 43–71. New York: Academic Press.

Bidwell, C. A.; Chrisman, C. L.; and Libey, G. S. 1985. Polyploidy induced by heat shock in channel catfish. *Aquaculture* 51:25–32.

Billard, R., and Richard, M. 1982. Inhibition of spermatogenesis and vitellogenesis in rainbow trout by hormonal additives in the diet. *Prog. Fish-Culturist* 44(1):15–18.

Borowsky, R. 1984. The evolutionary genetics of *Xiphophorus.* In *Evolutionary Genetics of Fishes,* 235–310. See Allendorf and Thorgaard, 1984.

Borowsky, R. L., and Kallman, K. D. 1976. Patterns of mating in natural populations of *Xiphophorus* (Pisces: Poeciliidae), I. *X. maculatus* from Belize and Mexico. *Evolution* 30:693–706.

Breider, H. 1935. Über Außenfaktoren, die das Geschlechtsverhältnis bei *Xiphophorus helleri* Heckel kontrollieren sollen. *Zeit. Wiss. Zool.* 146:383–416.

————. 1938. Die genetischen, histologischen und zytologischen Grundlagen der Geschwulstbildung nach Kreuzung verschiedener Rassen und Arten lebendgebärender Zahnkarpfen. *Zeit. Zellforsch.* 28:784–828.

Burtzev, I. A., and Serebryakova, E. V. 1973. A hybrid beluga X sterlet (*Husa huso* [L.] X *Acipenser ruthenus* [L.], Pisces): Karyology, gametogenesis and potential status. *Abstr. Proc. 13th Int. Congr. Genet. Genetics* 74:s35.

Cassani, J. R., and Caton, W. E. 1986. Efficient production of triploid grass carp (*Ctenopharyngodon idella*) utilizing hydrostatic pressure. *Aquaculture* 55:43–50.

Chevassus, B. 1983. Hybridization in fish. *Aquaculture* 33:245–62.

Childers, W. F. 1967. Hybridization of four species of sunfishes (Centrarchidae). III. *Nat. Hist. Surv. Bull.* 29:159–214.

Chourrout, D. 1982. Tetraploidy induced by heat shocks in rainbow trout *Salmo gairdneri* R. *Reprod. Nutr. Develop.* 22:569–74.

————. 1984. Pressure-induced retention of second polar body and suppression of first cleavage in rainbow trout: production of all-triploids, all-tetraploids and heterozygous and homozygous diploid gynogenetics. *Aquaculture* 36:111–26.

Clark, E. 1950. A method for artificial insemination in viviparous fishes. *Science* 112:722–23.

Clark, E.; Aronson, L. R.; and Gordon, M. 1954. Mating behavior patterns in two sympatric species of Xiphophorin fishes; their inheritance and significance in sexual isolation. *Bull. Am. Mus. Nat. Hist.* 103:135–226.

Conover, D. O., and Kynard, B. E. 1981. Environmental sex determination: Interaction of temperature and genotype in a fish. *Science* 213:577-79.

Dangel, J. R.; Macy, P. T.; and Withler, F. C. 1973. Annotated bibliography of interspecific hybridization of fishes of the subfamily Salmoninae. *National Oceanic and Atmospheric Administration Tech. Mem.*, NMFS NWFC 1. 48 pages.

Dildine, G. C. 1936. Studies on teleostean reproduction. I. Embryonic hermaphroditism in *Lebistes reticulatus. J. Morphol.* 60:261–77.

Donaldson, E. M., and Hunter, G. A. 1982. Sex control in fish with particular reference to salmonids. *Can. J. Fish. Aquat. Sci.* 39:99–110.

Dzwillo, M. 1959. Genetische Untersuchungen an domestizierten Stämmen von *Lebistes reticulatus* (Peters). *Mitt. Hamburgh. Zool. Mus. Inst.* 57:143–86.

————. 1962. Über künstliche Erzeugung funktioneller Männchen weiblichen Genotyps bei *Lebistes reticulatus. Bio. Zbl.* 81:575–84.

Echelle, A. A.; Echelle, A. F.; and Crozier, C. D. 1983. Evolution of an all-female fish, *Mendina clarkhubbsi* (Atherinidae). *Evolution* 37:772–84.

Echelle, A. A.; Wildrick, D. M.; and Echelle, A. F. 1989. Allozyme studies of genetic variation in poeciliid fishes. In *Ecology and Evolution of Livebearing Fishes (Poeciliidae)*, 217–34. *See* Angus 1989.

Entlinger, G. 1974. The brush-tail platy. *Trop. Fish Hobbyist* 22(1):95–98.

Ewulonu, J. K.; Haas, R.; and Turner, B. J. 1985. A multiple sex chromosome system in the annual killifish, *Nothobranchius guentheri. Copeia* 1985:503–508.

Farr, J. A. 1981. Biased sex ratios in laboratory strains of guppies, *Poecilia reticulata. Heredity* 47(2):237–48.

Ferris, S. D. 1984. Tetraploidy and the evolution of catostomid fishes. In *Evolutionary Genetics of Fishes*, 55-93. *See* Allendorf and Thorgaard 1984.

Gervai, J.; Peter, S.; Nagy, A.; et al. 1980. Induced triploidy in carp, *Cyprinus carpio* L. *J. Fish Biol.* 17:667–71.

Goodrich, H. B.; Dee, J. E.; Flynn, B. M.; et al. 1934. Germ cells and sex differentiation in *Lebistes reticulatus. Biol. Bull.* 67:83–96.

Goodrich, H. B.; Josephson, N. D.; Trinkaus, J. P.; et al. 1944. The cellular expression of two new genes in *Lebistes reticulatus. Genetics* 29:584–92.

Goodrich, H. B., and Smith, M. A. 1937. Genetics and histology of the colour pattern in the normal and albino paradise fish, *Macropodus opercularis* L. *Biol. Bull.* 73:527–34.

Gordon, M. 1927. The genetics of a viviparous top-minnow Platypoecilus: the inheritance of two kinds of melanophores. *Genetics* 12:253–83.

————. 1931. Morphology of the heritable color patterns in the Mexican killifish, *Platypoecilus. Am. J. Cancer* 15:732–87.

————. 1937. Genetics of *Platypoecilus.* 3. Inheritance of sex and crossing over of the sex chromosomes in the platyfish. *Genetics* 22:376–92.

————. 1942. Mortality of albino embryos and aberrant Mendelian ratios in certain broods of

Xiphophoru: helleri. Zoologica (N.Y.) 27:73–74.

———. 1946. ntrogressive hybridization in domesticated f shes. 1. The behavior of comet, a Platypoecilus maculatus gene in Xiphophorus helleri. Zoolo ica (N.Y.) 31:77–88.

———. 1947. G enetics of Platypoecilus maculatus. IV. The se x-determining mechanism in two wild populatic ns of the Mexican platyfish. Genetics 32:8–1'.

———. 1950. H redity of pigmented tumours in fish. Endeavou r 9:26–34.

———. 1951. Ge etics of Platypoecilus maculatus. V. Heterogamet c sex-determining mechanism in females of don esticated stocks originally from British Hondure s. Zoologica (N.Y.) 36:127–53.

———. 1952. Se determination in Xiphophorus (Platypoecilus) naculatus. III. Differentiation of gonads in platy ish from broods having a sex ratio of three fe males to one male. Zoologica (N.Y.) 37:91–10(.

———. 1955. Gu pies as Pets. Neptune City, N.J.: T.F.H. Publ cations. 32 pages.

———. 1956. An ntricate genetic system that controls nine pig nent cell patterns in the platyfish. Zoologica (I .Y.) 41:153–62.

Gordon, M., and Fra ser, A. 1931. Pattern genes in the platyfish. J. H ered. 22:169–85.

Grobstein, C. 1948. Optimal gonopodial morphogenesis in Platyp ecilus maculatus with constant dosage of nethyl testosterone. J. Exp. Zool. 109:215–33

Harrington, R. W., Jr. 1967. Environmentally controlled induction o primary male gonochorists from eggs of the s elf-fertilizing hermaphrodite fish, Rivulus mai noratus Poey. Biol. Bull. 131:174–99.

———. 1971. How ec ological and genetic factors interact to determi e when self-fertilizing hermaphrodites of Ri ulus marmoratus change into functional sec ndary males, with a reappraisal of the mod s of intersexuality among fishes. Copeia 1971 389–432.

Haskins, C. P., and Dr zba, J. P. 1938. Note on anomalous inheritan e of sex-linked color factors in the guppy. An Naturalist 72:571–74.

Haskins, C. P., and Has <ins, E. F. 1948. Albinism, a semilethal autoso nal mutation in Lebistes reticulatus. Heredity '(2):251–62.

Haskins, C. P.; Haskins, E. F.; McLaughlin, J. J. A.; et al. 1961. Polymc rphism and population structure in Lebistes eticulatus. In Vertebrate

Speciation, ed. W. Frank Blair, 320–95. Austin: University of Texas Press.

Haskins, C. P.; Young, P.; Hewitt, R. E.; et al. 1970. Stabilised heterozygosis of supergenes mediating certain Y-linked colour patterns in populations of Lebistes reticulatus. Heredity 25(4): 575–89.

Hearin, B. 1963. New introductions from the Delta Aquarium. Trop. Fish Hobbyist 12(1):5–14.

Heiligenberg, W. 1965. Color polymorphism in the males of an African cichlid fish. J. Zool. 146:95–97.

Hickling, C. F. 1960. The Malacca Tilapia hybrids. J. Genet. 57:1–10.

Hildemann, W. H. 1954. Effects of sex hormones on secondary sex characters of Lebistes reticulatus. J. Exp. Zool. 126:1–15.

Hubbs, C. L. 1940. Speciation of fishes. Am. Naturalist 74:198–211.

Hubbs, C. L., and Hubbs, L. C. 1932. Apparent parthenogenesis in nature, in a form of fish of hybrid origin. Science 76:628–30.

Hulata, G.; Wohlfarth, G. W.; and Rothbard, S. 1983. Progeny-testing selection of tilapia broodstocks producing all-male hybrid progenies—preliminary results. Aquaculture 33:263–68.

Hunter, G. A.; Donaldson, E. M.; Stoss, J.; et al. 1983. Production of monosex female groups of chinook salmon (Oncorhynchus tshawytscha) by the fertilization of normal ova with sperm from sex-reversed females. Aquaculture 33:355–64.

Kallman, K. D. 1965. Genetics and geography of sex determination in the poeciliid fish, Xiphophorus maculatus. Zoologica (N.Y.) 50:151–90.

———. 1968. Evidence for the existence of transformer genes for sex in the teleost Xiphophorus maculatus. Genetics 60:811–28.

———. 1970a. Sex determination and the restriction of pigment patterns to the X and Y chromosomes in populations of a poeciliid fish, Xiphophorus maculatus, from the Belize and Sibun rivers of British Honduras. Zoologica (N.Y.) 55:1–16.

———. 1970b. Different genetic basis of identical pigment patterns in two populations of platyfish, Xiphophorus maculatus. Copeia 1970: 472–87.

———. 1970c. Moon of a million faces. Trop. Fish World 1(5):4–7, 26, 36–37.

———. 1971. Inheritance of melanophore patterns and sex determination in the Montezuma swordtail, *Xiphophorus montezumae cortezi* Rosen. *Zoologica* (N.Y.) 56:77–94.

———. 1973. The sex-determining mechanism of the platyfish, *Xiphophorus maculatus.* In *Genetics and Mutagenesis of Fish,* 19–28. *See* Anders et al. 1973.

———. 1975. The platyfish, *Xiphophorus maculatus.* In *Handbook of Genetics.* 4, ed. R. C. King, 81–132. New York: Plenum Press.

———. 1983. The sex-determining mechanism of the poeciliid fish, *Xiphophorus montezumae,* and the genetic control of the sexual maturation process and adult size. *Copeia* 1983(3): 755–69.

———. 1984. A new look at sex determination in poeciliid fishes. In *Evolutionary Genetics of Fishes,* 95–171. *See* Allendorf and Thorgaard 1984.

———. 1989. Genetic control of size at maturity in *Xiphophorus.* In *Ecology and Evolution of Livebearing Fishes (Poeciliidae),* 163–84. *See* Angus 1989.

Kallman, K. D., and Atz, J. W. 1966. Gene and chromosome homology in fishes of the genus *Xiphophorus. Zoologica* (N. Y.) 51:107–35.

Kallman, K. D., and Borkoski, V. 1978. A sex-linked gene controlling the onset of sexual maturity in female and male platyfish (*Xiphophorus maculatus*), fecundity in females and adult size in males. *Genetics* 89:79–119.

Kallman, K. D., and Borowsky, R. 1972. The genetics of gonopodial polymorphism in two species of poeciliid fish. *Heredity* 28:297–310.

Kallman, K. D., and Brunetti, V. 1983. Genetic basis of three mutant color varieties of *Xiphophorus maculatus:* the gray, gold and ghost platyfish. *Copeia* 1983(1):170–81.

Kallman, K. D.; Schreibman, M. P.; and Borkoski, V. 1973. Genetic control of gonadotrop differentiation in the platyfish, *Xiphophorus maculatus* (Poeciliidae). *Science* (Wash., D.C.) 181: 678–80.

Karbe, L. 1961. Cytologische Untersuchung der Sterilitätserscheinungen bei anatolischen Zahnkarpfen, ein Beitrag zum Speziationsproblem. *Mitt. Hamburg. Zool. Mus. Inst.* 59:73–104.

Kincaid, H. L. 1983. Inbreeding in fish populations used for aquaculture. *Aquaculture* 33:215–27.

Kirpichnikov, V. S. 1981. *Genetic Bases of Fish Selection.* Berlin, Heidelberg: Springer-Verlag.

410 pages.

Knepper, M., and Knepper, N. 1963. Our marble lyretail mollies. *Trop. Fish Hobbyist* 12(3):5.

Kosswig, C. 1934. Farbfaktoren und Geschlechtsbestimmung (nach Untersuchungen an Zahnkarpfen). *Der Züchter* 6:40–47.

———. 1935. Über Albinismus bei Fischen. *Zool. Anzeig.* 110:41–47.

———. 1964. Polygenic sex determination. *Experientia* 20:190–99.

———. 1973. The role of fish in research on genetics and evolution. In *Genetics and Mutagenesis of Fish,* 3–16. *See* Anders et al. 1973.

Langhammer, J. K. 1982. Albinism in *Pelviachromis pulcher. Buntbarsche Bull.* 93:8.

Larr, E. C. 1977. So you want big male guppies! *Livebearers* 33:11.

Leslie, J. F. 1982. Linkage analysis of seventeen loci in poeciliid fish (genus *Poeciliopsis*). *J. Hered.* 73:19–23.

Lodi, E. 1981. Competition between palla and normal bearing spermatozoa of *Poecilia reticulata. Copeia* 1981(3):624–29.

MacIntyre, P. A. 1961. Crossing over within the macromelanophore gene in the platyfish, *Xiphophorus maculatus. Am. Naturalist* 95: 323–24.

Mires, D. 1977. Theoretical and practical aspects of the production of all male *Tilapia* hybrids. *Bamidgeh* 29:94–101.

Morizot, D. C., and Siciliano, M. J. 1979. Polymorphism, linkage and mapping of four enzyme loci in the fish genus *Xiphophorus. Genetics* 93:947–60.

———. 1982a. Protein polymorphisms, segregation in genetic crosses and genetic distances among fishes of the genus *Xiphophorus* (Poeciliidae). *Genetics* 102:539-56.

———. 1982b. Linkage of two enzyme loci in fishes of the genus *Xiphophorus* (Poeciliidae). *J. Hered.* 73:163–67.

———. 1984. Gene mapping in fishes and other vertebrates. In *Evolutionary Genetics of Fishes,* 173–234. See Allendorf and Thorgaard 1984.

Morizot, D. C.; Wright, D. A.; and Siciliano, M. J. 1977. Three linked enzyme loci in fishes: implications in the evolution of vertebrate chromosomes. *Genetics* 86:645–56.

Mrakovcic, M., and Haley, L. E. 1979. Inbreeding depression in the zebra fish *Brachydanio rerio* (Hamilton Buchana). *J. Fish. Biol.* 15:323–27.

Nayudu, P. L. 1979. Genetic studies of melanic

color patter is and atypical sex determination in the gup by, *Poecilia reticulata. Copeia* 1979(2):225 31.

Norton, J. 196 a. Inheritance of the hi-fin dorsal in swordtails and platies. *Trop. Fish Hobbyist* 15(5):45–49.

———. 1967b. rue hi-fin lyretail sword. *Trop. Fish Hobbyist* 16( ):4–9.

———. 1969. C enetics of red coral swordtails. *The Aquariun* 2(10):73–78.

———. 1970a. he veil swordtail. *The Aquarium* 3(3):32–33, 56 –58.

———. 1970b. hree colors of convict cichlids. *The Aquarium* 3(11):8–9, 52–53.

———. 1971a. / ngelfish—breeding and genetics. *The Aquar um* 6(10):34–41.

———. 1971b. G een angelfish and colorful discus. *The Aqua um* 5(1):8–13.

———. 1974. Ge etics of fancy mollies. *Today's Aquarist* 1(2):28 –36.

———. 1981. Cal co molly. *Freshwater and Marine Aquarium* 4 (7):22–24, 78–79.

———. 1982a. Anc elfish genetics: part one. *Freshwater and Marin Aquarium* 5(4):15–18, 90–91.

———. 1982b. A gelfish genetics: part two. *Freshwater and Marine Aquarium* 5(5):22–23.

———. 1982c. An elfish genetics: part three. *Freshwater and Marine Aquarium* 5(7):8–10, 91–92.

———. 1982d. Ar gelfish genetics: part four. *Freshwater and I larine Aquarium* 5(8):15–17.

———. 1982e. An elfish genetics: part five. *Freshwater and I larine Aquarium* 5(9):8–10.

———. 1982f. Angel ish genetics: part six. *Freshwater and Marine Aquarium* 5(10):38–40.

———. 1982g. Ang lfish genetics: part seven. *Freshwater and M rine Aquarium* 5(11):40–41.

———. 1983. Clowr angelfish. *Freshwater and Marine Aquarium* ((5):15–17, 89, 91.

———. 1984a. Black elvet angelfish. *Freshwater and Marine Aquaric m* 7(7):10–11.

———. 1984b. Red n ollies. *Freshwater and Marine Aquarium* 7(10 86–87.

———. 1985a. Leop rd angelfish. *Freshwater and Marine Aquariu n* 8(2):10–14.

———. 1985b. Half-b ack angelfish. *Freshwater and Marine Aquariu n* 8(8):18–23.

———. 1986. Peach m lly and other new mollies. *Freshwater and Mar e Aquarium* 9(9):12–17.

———. 1988. Gold ma ble angelfish. *Freshwater and Marine Aquariun* 11(9):88–90.

———. 1989. Half-blac combinations in angelfish. *Freshwater and Marine Aquarium* 12(5):26–28, 134.

———. 1990a. Seven kinds of marble angelfish. *Freshwater and Marine Aquarium* 13(5):127–29, 134–35.

———. 1990b. Pearly—a new angelfish mutation. *Freshwater and Marine Aquarium* 13(12):90–92.

Ojima, Y.; Uyeno, K.; and Hayashi, M. 1976. A review of the chromosome number in fishes. *Kromosome* II-1:19–47.

Ong, Y. W. 1960. The lyretail black molly, a new strain. *Trop. Fish Hobbyist* 8(12):24–34.

Onozato, H. 1983. Artificial polyploidization in fishes and its application in aquaculture. *Fish Genet. Breed. Sci.* (Suisan Ikushu) 8:17–29 (in Japanese).

Ostrow, M. E. 1978. Data on sex ratios. *Trop. Fish Hobbyist* 27:39–40.

———. 1979. Sex ratios and pH in platies. *Trop. Fish Hobbyist* 27:44–46.

Oztan, N. 1963. The effects of gonadotropic and steroid hormones on the gonads of sterile hybrid fishes. *Rev. Fac. Sci.* (Istanbul) B25:27–47.

Park, E. H. 1974. A list of the chromosome number of fishes. *Coll. Rev. Coll. Lab. Art Sci., Seoul Nat. Univ.* 20:346–72.

Prehn, L. M., and Rasch, E. M. 1969. Cytogenetic studies of *Poecilia* (Pisces): I. Chromosome numbers of naturally occurring poeciliid species and their hybrids from eastern Mexico. *Can. J. Genet. Cytol.* 11:888–95.

Pruginin, Y.; Rothbard, S.; Wohlfarth, G.; et al. 1975. All male broods of *Tilapia nilotica* X *T. aurea* hybrids. *Aquaculture* 6:11–21.

Purdom, C. E. 1983. Genetic engineering by the manipulation of chromosomes. *Aquaculture* 33:287–300.

Rasch, E. M., and Balsano, J. S. 1974. Biochemical and cytogenetic studies of *Poecilia* from eastern Mexico. II. Frequency, perpetuation, and probable origin of triploid genomes in females associated with *Poecilia formosa. Rev. Biol. Trop.* 21:351–81.

Rasch, E. M.; Darnell, R. M.; Kallman, K. D.; et al. 1965. Cytophotometric evidence for triploidy in hybrids of the gynogenetic fish, *Poecilia formosa. J. Exp. Zool.* 160:155–70.

Rauchenberger, M.; Kallman, K. D.; and Morizot, D. C. 1990. Monophyly and geography of the Río Pánuco basin swordtails (genus *Xiphophorus*) with descriptions of four new species.

Amer. Mus. Novitates No. 2975. 41 pages.

Rishi, K. K. 1979. Somatic G-banded chromosomes of *Colisa fasciatus* (Perciformes: Belontidae) and confirmation of female heterogamety. *Copeia* 1979(1):146–49.

Rosen, D. E. 1979. Fishes from the uplands and intermontane basins of Guatemala: revisionary studies and comparative geography. *Bull. Am. Mus. Nat. Hist.* 162(5):267–376.

Rubin, D. A. 1985. Effect of pH on sex ratio in cichlids and a poecilliid [sic] (Teleostei). *Copeia* 1985:233–35.

Schmidt, J. 1920. Racial investigations. IV. The genetic behavior of a secondary sexual character. *C. R. Trav. Lab.* (Carlsberg) 14(8):1–12.

Schreck, C. B., ed. 1974. *Control of Sex in Fishes.* Blacksburg: Virginia Polytechnic Institute and State University.

Schreibman, M. P., and Kallman, K. D. 1977. The genetic control of the pituitary-gonadal axis in the platyfish, *Xiphophorus maculatus. J. Exp. Zool.* 200:277–94.

Schröder, J. H. 1964. Genetische Untersuchungen an domestizierten Stämmen der Gattung *Mollienesia* (Poeciliidae). *Zool. Beiträge* 10(3):369–463.

———. 1966. Über Besonderheiten der Vererbung des Simpsonfaktors bei *Xiphophorus helleri* Heckel (Poeciliidae, Pisces). *Zool. Beiträge* (NF) 12:27–42.

———. 1969. Radiation-induced spermatogonial exchange between the X and Y chromosomes in the guppy. *Can. J. Genet. Cytol.* 11:948–54.

———, ed. 1973. *Genetics and Mutagenesis of Fish.* New York: Springer-Verlag. 356 pages.

Schultz, R. J. 1969. Hybridization, unisexuality and polyploidy in the teleost *Poeciliopsis* (Poeciliidae) and other vertebrates. *Am. Naturalist* 103:605–19.

———. 1977. Evolution and ecology of unisexual fishes. In *Evolutionary Biology,* ed. M. K. Hecht, W. C. Steere, and B. Wallace, Vol. 10, 277–331. New York: Plenum Press.

———. 1980. Role of polyploidy in the evolution of fishes. In *Polyploidy—Biological Relevance,* ed. W. H. Lewis, 313–40. New York: Plenum Press.

Schultz, R. J., and Kallman, K. D. 1968. Triploid hybrids between the all-female teleost *Poecilia formosa* and *Poecilia sphenops. Nature* 219:280–82.

Schwartz, F. J. 1972. World Literature to Fish Hybrids with an Analysis by Family, Species, and Hybrid. Ocean Springs, Miss: Gulf Coast Res. Lab. *Publ. Gulf Coast Res. Lab. Mus.* No. 3. 328 pages.

Seligmann, E. B., Jr. 1958. Factors governing color variations in angelfish. *The Aquarium* 27:176–79, 189.

Shami, S. A., and Beardmore, J. A. 1978. Genetic studies of enzyme variation in the guppy, *Poecilia reticulata* (Peters). *Genetica* 48:67–73.

Smith, M. W.; Smith, M. H.; and Chesser, R. K. 1983. Biochemical genetics of mosquitofish. I. Environmental heterogeneity of allele frequencies within a river drainage. *Copeia* 1983(1):182–93.

Sterba, G. 1959. Über eine Mutation bei *Pterophyllum eimekei*. I. Anamnese und Beschreibung. *Biol. Zentralbl.* 78:323–33.

Strommen, C. A.; Rasch, E. M.; and Balsano, J. S. 1975. Cytogenetic studies of *Poecilia.* V. Cytophotometric evidence for the production of fertile offspring by triploids related to *Poecilia formosa. J. Fish. Biol.* 7:1–10.

Sullivan, J. A., and Schultz, R. J. 1986. Genetic and environmental basis of variable sex ratios in laboratory strains of *Poeciliopsis lucida. Evolution* 40(1):152–58.

Suzuki, R., and Fukuda, Y. 1972. Growth and survival of F_1 hybrids among salmonid fishes. *Bull. Freshwater Fish. Res. Lab.* 21:117–38.

Takahashi, H. 1975. Functional masculinization of female guppies, *Poecilia reticulata,* influenced by methyltestosterone before birth. *Bull. Jpn. Soc. Sci. Fish.* 41:499–506.

Thorgaard, G. H.; Jazwin, M. E.; and Stier, A. R. 1981. Polyploidy induced by heat shock in rainbow trout. *Trans. Am. Fish. Soc.* 110:546–50.

Turner, B. J. 1982. The evolutionary genetics of a unisexual fish, *Poecilia formosa*. In *Mechanisms of Speciation,* 265–305. New York: Alan R. Liss.

Uyeno, T., and Miller, R. R. 1971. Multiple sex chromosomes in a Mexican cyprinodontid fish. *Nature* 231:452–53.

Valenti, R. J. 1975. Induced polyploidy in *Tilapia aurea* (Steindachner) by means of temperature shock treatment. *J. Fish Biol.* 7:519–28.

Vallowe, H. H. 1953. Some physiological aspects of reproduction in *Xiphophorus maculatus. Biol. Bull.* 104:240–49.

Van Oordt, G. J. 1928. The duration of life of the

spermatozoa in the fertilized female of *Xiphophorus helleri* Regan. *Tijds. Ned. Deerk. Vereen, Ser.* 3:77–80.

Winge, Ø. 1922. One-sided masculine and sex-linked inheritance in *Lebistes reticulatus*. *J. Genet.* 12:145–62.

———. 1927. The location of eighteen genes in *Lebistes reticulatus*. *J. Genet.* 18:1–42.

———. 1930. On the occurrence of XX males in *Lebistes*, with some remarks on Aida's so-called "nondisjunction" males in *Aplocheilus*. *J. Genet.* 23:69–76.

———. 1934. The experimental alteration of sex chromosomes and vice versa, as illustrated in *Lebistes*. *C. R. Trav. Lab. Carlsberg Ser. Physiol.* 21:1–49.

———. 1937. Succession of broods in *Lebistes*. *Nature* 140:467.

Winge, Ø., and Ditlevsen, E. 1938. A lethal gene in the Y-chromosome of *Lebistes*. *C. R. Trav. Lab. Carlsberg Ser. Physiol.* 22:203–10.

———. 1947. Colour inheritance and sex determination in *Lebistes*. *Heredity* 1:65–83.

Wohlfarth, G. W. 1983. Genetics of fish: applications to warm water fishes. *Aquaculture* 33:373–81.

Wohlfarth, G. W., and Hulata, G. I. 1981. *Applied genetics of tilapia*. International Center for Living Aquatic Resources Management, Studies and Reviews 6. 26 pages.

Wolfsheimer, G. 1960. The Simpson swordtail. *Aquar. J.* 31(11):544–45.

———. 1965. Latest in mollies. *Aquar. J.* 36(6): 274–76.

Wolters, W. R.; Libey, G. S.; and Chrisman, C. L. 1981. Induction of triploidy in channel catfish. *Trans. Am. Fish. Soc.* 110:310–12.

———. 1982. Effect of triploidy on growth and gonad development of channel catfish. *Trans. Am. Fish. Soc.* 111:102–105.

Wood, J. A. 1968. A new molly. *The Aquarium* 1(5):6.

Yamamoto, T. 1953. Artificially induced sex-reversal in genotypic males of the medaka (*Oryzias latipes*). *J. Exp. Zool.* 123:571–94.

———. 1955. Progeny of artificially induced sex reversals of male genotype (XY) in the medaka (*Oryzias latipes*) with special reference to YY-male. *Genetics* 40:406–19.

———. 1958. Artificial induction of functional sex-reversal in genotypic females of the medaka (*Oryzias latipes*). *J. Exp. Zool.* 137:227–62.

———. 1962. Hormonic factors affecting gonadal sex differentiation in fish. *Gen. Comp. Endocrinol. Suppl.* 1:341–45.

———. 1969. Sex differentiation. In *Fish Physiology*, ed. W. S. Hoar and D. J. Randall, Vol. III, 117–75. New York: Academic Press.

———. 1975. The medaka, *Oryzias latipes*, and the guppy, *Lebistes reticularis* [sic]. In *Handbook of Genetics*, 133–49. See Kallman 1975.

Yamazaki, F. 1983. Sex control and manipulation in fish. *Aquaculture* 33:329–54.

Zander, C. D. 1969. Über die Entstehung und Veränderung von Farbmustern in der Gattung *Xiphophorus* (Pisces). I. Qualitative Veränderungen nach Artkreuzung. *Mitt. Hamb. Zool. Mus. Inst.* 66:241–71.

Breeding Aquarium Fish

Paul V. Loiselle

It is widely believed that much expert knowledge is required to induce most tropical fish species to spawn successfully in captivity. This simply is not true. Certain easily mastered fundamentals are common to nearly all cases. In addition, fish can be divided into several operational groups based upon common features of their reproductive biology. Within these reproductive guilds, members can be handled in much the same manner in captivity. In the pages that follow, both general guidelines and more specific pointers are presented. Anyone willing to read them carefully and to follow the procedures outlined therein can expect to spawn and rear an enormous variety of aquarium fish successfully.

These are not the only approaches that will work under home aquarium conditions, nor do I make any pretense of having covered the topic of this chapter exhaustively. Due to space limitations, fascinating details of the basic reproductive biology of these groups have been omitted. Readers are urged to consult the references at the chapter's end, and the often extensive bibliographies contained therein, as a useful starting point to increase their knowledge and enhance their mastery of aquarium fish breeding, the most interesting and challenging aspect of the aquarium hobby.

Basic Reproductive Patterns of Aquarium Fishes		
Category	Characteristics	Selected Examples
Live-Bearers		
	Females deliver live young.	poeciliids (guppies, mollies, platys, swordtails), goodeids, halfbeaks
Egg Layers With No Parental Care		
Type 1 egg scatterers	Young pass through yolk-sac developmental stage between egg and fully mobile fry.	danios, rasboras, kissing gourami, monos, barbs, tetras, Corydoras, loaches, glassfish
Type 2 egg scatterers	Young fully mobile upon hatching; no diapause (period of arrested development).	silversides and allied atherinids, rainbowfishes, cyprinodontid killifish
Annual fishes	Eggs go through diapause; adults with rapid growth and short life-span.	killifish adapted for ephemeral habitats

Basic Reproductive Patterns of Aquarium Fishes		
Category	Characteristics	Selected Examples
Egg Layers That Practice Parental Care		
Paternal custodial species	Males care for eggs and zygotes; usually polygamous. Well-developed spawning site preferences.	
Aphrophils	Bubble nest builders; usually able to breathe atmospheric oxygen.	many Belontiidae and Anabantidae, including Betta, Colisa, Cetenopoma
Speleophils	Spawn in cavities, either naturally occurring or ones they have constructed. Typically inhabit well-oxygenated habitats.	gobies, sticklebacks, armored suckermouth catfishes, darter perch, sculpins
Agoraphils, Phytophils	Spawn in the open upon plants, solid surfaces, or in nest in sand or gravel.	Copella, Polycentrus, Gymnarchus, Bagrus, sunfishes
Paternal brooders	Males cary zygotes until eggs hatch or fry are free-swimming.	Osteoglossum, Glossamia, Betta, Loricaria, Luciocephalus, some cichlids
Biparental custodial species	Both parents care for eggs; parents are monogamous. May be agoraphils, speleophils, or mouthbrooders.	Monogamous substratum-spawning cichlids; some piranhas and snakeheads; Arapaima
Maternal custodial species	female cares for eggs; polygamous or polygynous. Speleophils or mouthbrooders.	Scleropages; polygamous cichlids, e.g. Apistogramma, Nanochromis, Haplochromis, Oreochromis

General Guidelines for Breeding Aquarium Fish

Use of fairly large aquaria with tight covers, careful monitoring of the breeding pair, and attention to the nutritional requirements of the newly mobile offspring, called fry, do much to assure reproductive success for any aquarium species. Other commonalities are outlined below. Supplement the information given here with more specific guidelines in the later sections of this chapter.

Pairing and aggression: The mating system of a great many fish is based upon territoriality and aggression. Fighting can have serious consequences if the defeated contender cannot move beyond the reach of the victor. In most cases, to avoid loss of prized fish, one simply must house species in tanks large enough to allow each sex to keep out of each other's way and with plentiful hiding places. Determination of minimum tank size often can be made only on a species-by-species basis and requires a certain amount of research. Err on the side of caution.

Tank management: In addition to the regular aquarium, one or more separate tanks usually must be established for various aspects of the breeding procedure, such as conditioning the breeders, spawning, or rearing the fry. Each of these must be provided with a mature sponge filter, properly treated water, and a sealed thermostatic heater. The nitrogen cycle in each must also be managed carefully through a system of regular partial water changes.

To maximize the likelihood of very young fry encountering prey, water level in a rearing tank is often lowered to one-quarter or one-third of its maximum capacity at first. As the young grow larger, the water level is slowly raised until the tank is completely full. Lowering the water level in this manner will not adversely affect sponge filter operation, but the heater should be tilted at an angle as necessary to keep it properly submerged.

Conditioning: In many cases, it is desirable to move potential breeders into separate tanks for special attention aimed at getting them into top reproductive condition. The two sexes should be housed separately and fed two or three times a day with a diet high in live or frozen high-protein foods, such as wingless fruit flies, frozen bloodworms, white or Grindal worms, glassworms, adult brine shrimp, or where appropriate, small fish. Tubificid worms pose some risk of systemic bacterial infection in aquarium fish and should not be used as food.

Use of a delivery tank: Because of the widespread occurrence of cannibalism, a delivery tank is often necessary when breeding live-bearing fishes. Its size must reflect both that of the female and her expected fecundity, for in most cases it will serve as the initial rearing tank for the fry born therein. In general, its water should be of the same chemical makeup and temperature as the female's former quarters. A tight cover for the tank is an excellent investment, for many of these fish are excellent jumpers, particularly when skittish from being moved.

In most cases, a sponge filter poses minimal risk to fry, and its associated microfauna often provide an important dietary supplement. An established sponge filter should be allowed to operate for a day or so before the gravid female is introduced, to spare her the necessity of experiencing the fluctuations in nitrite concentration typical of a new tank. The delivery aquarium should experience the same daily light/dark cycle as the female's previous residence.

Feeding fry: The fry of many species initially require infusoria. Culturing these microorganisms requires a certain amount of practice. There is always an element of chance with regard to which infusorians will predominate in a given culture, and not all are equally satisfactory as fry food. Microworms are a more easily cultured alternative and more nutritionally consistent. When feeding either infusoria or microworms, introduce as little of the culture medium as possible into the rearing tank. Even small quantities can fuel a potentially dangerous bacterial bloom.

Artemia (brine shrimp) nauplii are the largest of the living foods commonly used for fry. They are easily hatched in quantity on relatively short notice, are both nutritious and highly palatable to fry, and pose minimal risk of introducing potentially dangerous microorganisms into the rearing tank. Successful fish breeders rely upon them as fry food whenever possible.

Several feedings a day ensure maximum growth, but each feeding must be small. Microworms and nauplii both die within a few hours of being added to the water and once dead, decay rapidly. The short-term danger is that this organic matter will generate a bacterial bloom; the long-term hazard is the potential for the buildup of toxic nitrites produced by the organic matter's breakdown.

Managing the rearing tank: Frequent partial water changes are the easiest way to maintain a suitable growing environment in a closed system. Begin with changes of 10 percent of the tank's volume, with an increase to up to 80 percent every other day to encourage maximal growth once the fry have been moved to larger rearing tanks. The interval between changes can be extended through the use of chemically active media such as Poly-Filter™ or ChemiPure™.

Cannibalism: In general, if a breeder desires optimal survival of fry, one must be prepared to sort growing fry by size, as larger ones will eat smaller siblings. Some recommend that only the largest individuals in a tankful of fry be reared to maturity. However, because of a widespread phenomenon known as male growth superiority, the fastest growing and largest individuals in a spawn usually prove to be males. Thus, culling usually is better limited to the elimination of individuals that show obvious physical or colorational abnormalities.

Selective breeding: One often hears complaints that the current aquarium strains of some fish are not the equals of wild stock or even of the aquarium strains of a few decades past. Few populations of ornamental fish have been maintained in captivity long enough for true inbreeding depression to have occurred. Rather, such deterioration stems from a lack of selective breeding. The only way to maintain a quality strain of any fish is to select the most colorful and vigorous individuals for future breeding stock, rather than relying upon chance sexual encounters.

Live-Bearing Fishes

Species that deliver live young are a distinct minority, but include many of the most popular and

The distinctive tail spike of this male red swordtail (*Xiphophorus helleri*) is a unique feature of this popular live-bearer. However, the distinction between the male's rodlike gonopodium and the female's unmodified anal fin is a feature common to all poeciliids.

generally available ornamental fishes.

Basic biology relevant to the breeding of live-bearing fishes: All live-bearing fishes are characterized by internal fertilization. In some families (Anablepidae, Jeneysiidae, Poeciliidae), the male's anal fin has been modified into a specialized, phalluslike structure, the gonopodium. In the freshwater stingrays, the male's ventral fins have been modified to perform this function. Sperm transfer in the Goodeidae and the Hemiramphidae occurs through direct contact between the cloacal openings of the male and female. In the pipefish, the female deposits her eggs in the male's brood pouch, where fertilization occurs.

Live-bearing fishes span the continuum from ovoviviparity, in which the female produces heavily yolked eggs that contain all the stored food the developing embryo will require, through true viviparity, in which the young are directly connected to and nourished by the female's circulatory system. Such distinctions have considerable bearing on the care of gravid individuals. Ovoviviparous live-bearers seem more prone to miscarriage, while the nutritional demands of gravid viviparous females are greater.

The usual developmental interval in live-bearing fishes ranges from twenty-eight to thirty-two days, with an extreme of almost a year in freshwater sting rays and the surfperches of the family Embrotocidae. The length of this interval is influenced by ambient temperature, photoperiod, the female's nutritional state, and age. The interval between broods is shorter when females are well nourished and housed at the upper end of their preferred temperature range. In a number of poeciliid species, females deliver small broods of fry every few days because eggs are fertilized as they mature rather than being fertilized only after a batch has accumulated.

Once the female has dropped her young, she becomes receptive to male courtship. The apparently continuous interest most male live-bearers display in the cloacal region of accessible females represents an effort to monitor their reproductive status. The interval of female receptivity is brief, and in nature, competition for access to such females is intense.

In species in which the sexes differ little in size or males are the larger sex, especially those characterized by sharp sexual dimorphism, the female may suffer injury unless the fish are housed in a tank large enough to allow her to escape male attentions. Alternatively, such species can be housed in multi-female groups, which forces a male to divide his attentions among all the females present.

Among those species in which the female is larger, the female has a greater say in the selection of her consort. For the male, merely approaching the female may pose a risk ranging from predation to emasculation. These species should be housed only in tanks large enough to allow each sex to keep out of the other's way and should be provided with plenty of cover. Determination of suitable tank size can be made only on a species-by-species basis and requires a certain amount of research.

Determinate male growth: In many poeciliid species, further linear growth ceases once a male's anal fin undergoes its metamorphosis to become the gonopodium. The mature male may become deeper-bodied, but he does not grow any longer. Thus, late-maturing males grow larger than early-maturing ones. The factors that determine the onset of gonopodial metamorphosis are complex. Genetic factors largely determine the onset of male reproductive maturity, and many wild populations have both early-maturing and late-maturing males. Where living conditions fluctuate markedly and in an unpredictable fashion, early-maturing males predominate. Where the environment is more predictable and living conditions more stable, the late-maturing males are more common.

Aquarium conditions seem to favor the smaller early-maturing male, perhaps because limited swimming space tends to make the hit-and-run approach to courtship of early-maturing males disproportionately effective. The buildup of metabolites that typically occurs when fry are reared in aquaria also appears to trigger early gonopodial metamorphosis and consequent male stunting. When members of a species not known to manifest this genetic polymorphism are raised in an environment where metabolic wastes are not allowed to accumulate, males mature later and average larger than counterparts reared under closed conditions. The implications of this phenomenon on the aquarium husbandry of these fishes are obvious.

Sex reversal: In some *Xiphophorus* and *Poecilia* species, old females develop the full array of secondary male sex characteristics, including metamorphosis of the anal fin into a gonopodium.

However, while they look like males, documented evidence of functional sex changes in these fish is lacking. Like many lower vertebrates, poeciliids have gonads that are comprised of both testicular and ovarian elements. As long as it remains functional, the dominant element suppresses the activity of the subordinate. Female poeciliids have only a finite number of follicles in their ovaries capable of maturing into eggs. Once a female has exhausted these, the dominant ovarian element of her gonads no longer produces the hormones that suppress the activity of their testicular analog. Secondary development of female characteristics in older males appears not to occur because there is no such built-in limitation on testicular activity.

Management of gravid females: Representatives of seven families of live-bearing fishes are more or less frequently kept as freshwater residents. Most of these fish breed regularly without any encouragement from their keeper. The central problem facing the prospective breeder is that of saving as many fry as possible from being devoured. Cannibalism varies in intensity from one species to the next. In some instances, newly dropped fry are ignored by conspecifics unless the latter are themselves poorly fed. One need only set a pair or trio up alone in a well-planted 80- to 120-liter (20- to 30-gallon) tank and feed the adults generously to breed these species sucessfully. Once fry appear, offer appropriate food on a regular schedule. Remove older fry to a separate rearing tank to make room for younger siblings and to provide an environment that promotes optimal growth.

Other live-bearers are so predatory that such an approach will not give satisfactory results under aquarium conditions. In these cases, a special delivery tank is needed (see previous section, "General Guidelines"). A 40- to 60-liter (10- to 15-gallon) aquarium suffices for most commonly raised species. Provide a dense layer of floating vegetation to shelter the newly delivered fry and a tight cover to keep the skittish female from jumping out.

In general, it is unwise to move a gravid female later than a week prior to the anticipated delivery date. The closer her projected delivery date, the more vulnerable she is to stress-induced miscarriage. With larger species such as the sailfin mollies, swordtails, and more robust goodeids, avoid any serious trauma later than ten days prior to

The dark gravid spot visible over the vent of the female of this pair of variatus platys (*Xiphophorus variatus*) occurs in many poeciliid and goodeid species.

delivery. These fish tend to struggle more actively when netted, and thus run a greater risk of injuring themselves and their brood.

If a female's prior reproductive history is unknown, err on the side of caution and isolate the female as soon as her flanks show signs of swelling when seen from above. Once a female has dropped her fry, the next delivery date can be easily projected.

With most live-bearing species, developing fry will cause the female to fill out noticeably. In many cases, the eyes of the young become clearly visible through the body wall a few days before delivery. Some poeciliids and goodeids have a conspicuous dark area over the vent, known as the gravid spot, which tends to become darker as the female's pregnancy advances.

Feed the female generously with a combination of commercially available conditioning foods and live and frozen foods. As soon as the condition of the female's abdomen indicates that birth is imminent, keep live food such as *Daphnia* constantly present in the delivery tank. Postpartum adults have a ravenous appetite, and the availability of alternative foods may reduce the incidence of maternal cannibalism. If this is not possible, the female should be checked as frequently as possible and removed immediately after dropping her fry. Females usually begin delivering at first light and are done by noon.

Use of breeding traps: A breeding trap is often recommended to allow newly delivered fry to drop out of the female's reach, either into a delivery tank or into a separate compartment of a plastic box suspended from the tank rim. Regrettably, commercially available breeding traps are far too small to accommodate most gravid female live-bearers for any length of time. The detainee typically struggles frantically to escape, and in so doing, she is likely to miscarry. The longer she is restrained, the more likely a gravid female is to injure herself, but delaying the gravid female's transfer into the trap risks premature delivery.

As a rule of thumb, never attempt to use a breeding trap with any female live-bearer whose total length is equal to or greater than the minimum depth of the compartment into which she would be placed. Even so, one has no guarantee that a female will accept such limitations on her movements. Many of the smaller goodeids simply do not tolerate confinement in a breeding trap.

As a safer alternative, a day or two before the female's expected delivery, reduce the water level in the tank to a depth of 15 to 20 centimeters (6 to 8 inches), then cover the bottom with Java moss and the surface with floating plants such as foxtail and floating fern. This will severely limit the female's mobility without triggering self-destructive behavior. The fry, on the other hand, can slip easily between the stems and leaves.

A delay in delivery of a few days usually stems from an excessively optimistic projection of the female's due date rather than from the operation of any complicating factors. Be patient. Intervention is apt to provoke premature birth, and the prognosis for premature fry is not favorable.

It is sometimes recommended that the female be given the opportunity to recuperate for a few days before being returned to a community tank or reintroduced to the presence of males. Assuming her original home is well planted and other females are present to distract the attention of amorous males, such sequestration is not necessary.

Rearing live-bearer fry: Once the fry are born and the female removed, bring the water level in the tank back up to normal again. Most live-bearer fry can take finely powdered prepared foods for their first meal, but also greatly relish live foods such as *Artemia* nauplii and microworms. Give several small feedings daily to ensure maximum growth. Fry reared in a long-established, well-lit, planted aquarium, with its associated community of microscopic organisms, typically grow faster and more uniformly than those reared in bare aquaria. Fry can remain in the delivery tank for their first month, then should be transferred to more spacious quarters. Breeder flats of 120 to 160 liters (30 to 40 gallons) can provide excellent housing for up to fifty fry.

Change part of the water frequently (see "General Guidelines"). Inattention to proper tank maintenance can quickly lead to mass mortality and/or a tank of stunted individuals.

Promptly segregate the sexes as soon as they can be reliably distinguished. The ability of many poeciliids to store sperm means that a single chance sexual encounter can eliminate a female for life from a planned breeding program. Males of most live-bearers become functional well before secondary sexual color or finnage distinctions develop fully, but with practice it is possible to recognize males before they attain reproductive competence.

Egg Layers That Do Not Practice Parental Care

Some egg layers practice parental care; others do not. The former modify the environment in a manner that favors the survival of their otherwise vulnerable zygotes. The latter seek out the microhabitat that affords their zygotes the best chance for successful development. Prospective breeders must carefully recreate such an environment in the spawning tank. To facilitate this task, the great many species of fish in this category are divided into subgroups (see the table at the beginning of this chapter).

Most egg-scattering fishes can be readily classified, but a few species defy facile classification. The zygotes of the pygmy sunfish (*Elassoma evergladei*) develop in the type 1 manner, but the adults display a type 2 spawning pattern.

Breeding Techniques for Type 1 Egg Scatterers

Egg scatterers include a large number of species with highly idiosyncratic reproductive behavior and management requirements. Thorough research is thus needed to set up an appropriate breeding tank. Seek the advice of other aquarists who have successfully bred the species in question under local conditions. Their experience will often supplement published accounts in a useful manner.

Rearing, selecting, and conditioning breeding stock: It is better to purchase ten to twelve juvenile fish and rear them to sexual maturity rather than buy a "proven" breeding pair or trio. Young adults are typically more vigorous and fertile than older individuals. Many type 1 egg scatterers display secondary sex differences less obvious than those of live-bearing fishes. In general, female type 1 egg scatterers (those whose young pass through a yolk-sac developmental stage) are heavier bodied than males and typically look much fuller in the flanks when seen from above. Depending upon their mating system, the females may be either larger or smaller than the males. Males generally are more brightly colored than females and often have longer or more elaborate finnage. The anal fins of male characins and some allied fishes are covered with minute hooks that will catch briefly in a fine-meshed net.

Fish large enough to be sexed are old enough to be spawned successfully, and should be moved into separate conditioning tanks for seven to ten days and fed with high-protein foods (see "General Guidelines").

Males are typically ready to breed sooner than females. Ripe females of most species appear visibly full, especially when examined from above. In "translucent" species, the ovaries of ripe females will appear notably more granular than do the testes of males when the fish are viewed against strong backlighting.

Setting up the spawning tank: A covered all-glass aquarium is recommended. For the smaller characoids, barbs, and rasboras, 20 liters (5 gallons) will suffice; for robust and prolific species, tank capacity should be 80 liters (20 gallons) to 140 liters (35 gallons).

Because of the zygotes' sensitivity to bacterial attack, the spawning tank must be carefully sterilized before being used. Fill the tank half full of tap water as hot as is briefly bearable, then add 1/2 cup (120 milliliters) of liquid laundry bleach (5.25 percent sodium hypochlorite) per liter or quart of water. Wearing kitchen gloves, use the resulting solution to wash both its interior and the glass cover thoroughly with a previously unused kitchen sponge. Drain the bleach solution, rinse the tank thoroughly with very hot tap water, then cover it tightly and allow it to cool to room temperature. That portion of the heater to be submerged in the spawning tank and any gravel, rockwork, or plastic appliances should be treated likewise. This may seem a very dangerous means of preventing the entry of bacteria into the spawning tank. However, under elevated water temperatures, chlorine bleach breaks down to yield chlorine, which leaves the water as a gas, and common table salt, which is quite harmless to fish.

Filling the spawning tank: If the species to be bred will spawn readily in tap water, it is a simple matter to fill the tank with extremely hot water, put the heater and other appliances in place, cover the tank tightly, and allow it to cool overnight. Then plug in the heater, connect a mature sponge filter, add an appropriate spawning substratum, and the tank is ready for use. If water in the

Scrupulous attention to both water chemistry and tank cleanliness is essential when working with type 1 egg scatterers from "blackwater" habitats, such as the cardinal tetra (*Paracheirodon axelrodi*).

breeding tank must be made harder and more alkaline, appropriate additives should be dissolved in hot water and added to the tank immediately after it has been filled. Salts go into solution more readily in hot water.

Species from "blackwater" habitats will breed successfully only in nearly sterile acid water with no detectable hardness. Blackwater is characterized as being soft, highly acidic, and in nature stained a dark reddish color from decayed plant matter. The simplest method is to begin with deionized water, available at most supermarkets by the gallon. Add Tetra's Blackwater Extract™ according to manufacturer's instructions. Once the desired pH value has been reached, add a level teaspoon (5 milliliters) of table salt (sodium chloride) per liter or quart of treated water to provide the small quantities of dissolved salts which are present in naturally occurring blackwater but are absent from deionized water. Finally, sterilize this solution by boiling it for several minutes in a glass vessel which is then covered, immediately removed from the heat, and allowed to cool to room temperature. Blackwater so treated can be stored in sealed vessels until needed or added directly to the spawning tank.

Selecting a spawning substrate: Live plants should be employed only for those species with zygotes which can tolerate substantial numbers of bacteria in their environment. Java moss is well accepted by most of these species, can be rinsed under a vigorous stream of water without damage, and prospers under the dim illumination characteristic of most breeding setups.

Alternative spawning substrata include bunches of washed willow roots and Spanish moss, both of which have been used for decades by commercial fish breeders. More readily available to the home aquarist are the finer grades of reusable plastic filter floss (well accepted by the smaller species) and "mops" of nylon yarn (see under "Breeding Techniques for Type 2 Egg Scatterers"). As a rule, fish prefer to place their eggs on dark-colored substrata.

Some type 1 egg scatterers produce nonadhesive eggs. These fish spawn over coarse gravel bottoms in nature. One can easily construct a spawning grid from two pieces of plastic egg crate diffuser grating, one cut to the exact internal dimension of the spawning tank, the other cut one cell row shorter in both length and width. Offset the smaller piece half a cell row inward from their common edges and bond the two together with cyanoacrylate glue. Such a grid is easily sterilized. Placed so the shorter of the two pieces rests on the aquarium bottom, the grid affords eggs excellent protection from cannibalism while assuring adequate water circulation around them. Remove the grid immediately after spawning once the adults have left the tank.

Induction of spawning: In nature, many type 1 egg scatterers spawn in the wake of the moderate spates produced by a rainstorm. Such localized precipitation briefly lowers water temperature 1 or 2 degrees C (2 or 4 degrees F). To duplicate this important environmental stimulus, the water in the breeding tank should initially be somewhat cooler than that of the conditioning aquaria.

Introduce the plumpest female and most brightly colored male into the breeding tank in the evening, taking care to acclimate them to its slightly cooler water. (Do not feed them! To do so is to encourage the sort of bacterial growth you have been at pains to prevent.) Slightly adjust the thermostat setting of the heater to allow the water temperature to rise overnight to that of the conditioning aquaria. Left together overnight, most species will spawn at first light.

Check the fish in the morning. If spawning has occurred, the female will have a distinctly deflated appearance. Eggs will appear as tiny glass beads scattered through the spawning material or over the tank bottom. Remove the breeders at once. If spawning has not occurred, allow the fish the remainder of the day together.

If by the end of this time, no eggs are present,

Some type 1 egg scatterers, such as *Rasbora heteromorpha*, are more readily induced to spawn in captivity if set up as groups rather than as single pairs.

remove the original pair. Siphon off any fecal matter from the bottom of the spawning tank and discard it along with its accompanying water. Remove half of the remaining water, and replace it with cooler sterile water of the same chemical makeup. (The water that has been drawn off can be rendered usable again by boiling.) Introduce another pair from the pool of breeding stock, or, if only a single pair is available, feed them heavily for several days and try them again.

Some references recommend that type 1 egg scatterers be spawned in trios of two males to a single female. The possible advantages must be balanced against the certain disadvantage of a third hungry mouth once spawning is completed. The same holds true for the group breeding recommended for some hard-to-breed species. A larger aquarium will be necessary when using more than a single pair of fish.

Care of developing zygotes: Not uncommonly, a small percentage of the eggs fail to develop normally, usually because they were never fertilized. Dead eggs become opaque due to bacterial activity and may rapidly develop a fluffy appearance due to a saprophytic fungus, *Saprolegnia.* Left untreated, the dead organic material in the water can fuel a substantial bacterial bloom under some conditions. Resistance to bacterial and fungal attack varies greatly; as a rule, the zygotes of blackwater species are most vulnerable. It may be necessary to experiment a bit with available antibacterial agents before finding a suitable treatment. Used according to the manufacturer's instructions, MarOxy™, a commercial medication featuring stabilized chlorine oxides as active ingredients, appears effective.

Zygotes typically hatch from twelve to forty-eight hours after spawning. The yolk-sac fry look like tiny glass slivers or commas with conspicuous dark eyes. Sometime between four and seven days after hatching, they become free-swimming fry which must be fed.

Rearing the fry: Type 1 egg-scatterer fry must be offered live food of a suitable size (see under "General Guidelines"). *Artemia* and many infusorians are attracted to light, whereas most blackwater fry are photophobic. Lowering the water level in the tank by one-half to two-thirds will increase the probability that the fry and their intended food will encounter one another. As a rule, the frys' light aversion disappears in about three weeks as they develop their species-typical color pattern. Once they have reached this point, the tank should be refilled to its full volume, and the fry are also large enough to take finely powdered prepared foods.

Excess organic matter from overfeeding causes the biggest danger in this early period. To minimize the risk of overfeeding, provide many small feedings daily. As additional insurance, one may add a dozen or so ramshorn or Malaysian live-bearing snails to the rearing tank as soon as the fry become mobile.

Newly mobile fry are weak swimmers and cope poorly with strong currents. Initially, allow only enough air to flow through the sponge filter unit to gently agitate the water surface. During this time, rinse the sponge cartridge regularly under lukewarm running water to keep its surface free of blockage. As the fry grow, increase the rate of water flow through the cartridge, which will correspondingly reduce the risk of surface blockage.

Daily siphoning of the tank bottom and replacement of 5 to 10 percent of its total volume with thoroughly dechlorinated fresh water of the same temperature and chemical makeup is recommended for all type 1 egg-scatterer fry, and is absolutely essential for particularly delicate species. As the fry grow older, increase the amount of water replaced and extend the interval between water changes to every four to seven days. When rearing species that require chemical modification of replacement water, a chemically active medium such as Polyfilter™ placed in a supplemental inside box filter or an air-driven outside filter will allow less frequent water changes without endangering growing fry.

Begin reducing the population density of fish per volume of water once they have developed their species-typical pattern of dark pigment. If the largest individuals present are more than twice again the size of the smallest, sort by size in order to avoid sibling cannibalism.

Breeding Techniques for Type 2 Egg Scatterers Without Diapause

Type 2 egg scatterers (those whose young hatch fully mobile) represent a smaller and considerably more homogeneous assemblage of fishes than type 1, but one still must research the biological idiosyncrasies of a given species to maximize the chances of a successful spawning effort. Popular representatives of this group are the killifishes

(Family: Cyprinodontidae), Australasian rainbow-fishes (Family: Melanotaeniidae), sailfin rainbow-fishes (Family: Telmatherinidae), Madagascar rainbowfishes (Family: Bedotiidae), and ricefishes (Family: Oryzatiidae). In much of the older aquarium literature, killifish and other type 2 egg scatterers are characterized as being difficult to breed successfully in captivity. In reality, they are more easily induced to spawn than most type 1 egg scatterers.

The zygotes of some type 2 species (those in this section) develop without interruption from fertilization through hatching. Those of others (the annual fishes) are characterized by the normal occurrence of a diapause, or period of arrested developmental activity. The breeding requirements of annual fishes will be discussed in a later section.

Selection of breeding stock: Many type 2 egg scatterers have rather short life-spans and display a pronounced drop-off in fecundity and male sexual capacity with increasing age. This trend is most pronounced among killifishes. Large individuals with impressive finnage usually make poor breeding stock. At an early age, type 2 egg scatterers become strongly sexually dimorphic in both color and fin development, so one is easily assured of having both sexes. However, there are advantages to having several individuals of each sex available. Females spawn a restricted number of eggs at a time, and in species in which males drive vigorously, setting up trios of one male and two females spares the females physical abuse.

To prevent uncontrolled spawning and to keep inter-male aggression within bounds, maintain males and females in separate tightly covered conditioning aquaria. Most species can be maintained on prepared food, but feeding females heavily with live and high-protein frozen foods will maximize egg production. If feeding white worms, alternate them with other high-roughage foods (such as crustaceans and insects) to avoid fatty degeneration of the gonads.

Preparation of the spawning tank: There are two approaches to breeding these fishes in captivity. In the continuous setup, the breeders are maintained in a heavily planted tank and allowed to breed *ad libitum.* The fry are reared together with the adults and require only the regular and generous provision of small food such as *Artemia* nauplii. Adults of most type 2 egg scatterers will disregard their progeny if heavily fed, but fry can also be removed to a separate rearing tank as soon as they are noticed. Do not keep snails in the tank, as they will efficiently seek out and devour fish eggs. This method does not produce large numbers of fry, but demands minimal effort from the breeder.

The hunt-and-pick approach requires the aquarist to harvest eggs from an artificial spawning substratum on a regular basis and incubate them separately. The tank size, furnishings, and water condition should be appropriate for the species being bred, but scrupulous attention to cleanliness is less important than for type 1 egg scatterers, as the eggs will not remain therein for any length of time after spawning.

Spawning mop construction: Manufactured spawning substrates are well accepted by these fish, but are not well designed for easy removal of eggs. Hence most serious breeders construct "spawning mops" out of nontoxic synthetic yarns.

Spawning mops can be constructed in several ways. Deep green or brown, 100 percent synthetic, guaranteed colorfast materials must be used. Their construction is relatively time-consuming, but one should produce a mop whose strands will not become tangled and which can be placed on the tank bottom for those type 2 egg scatterers which display a strong aversion to spawning near the water's surface. Make several mops to offer a male a choice of spawning sites and females a choice of hiding places.

Newly constructed mops should be soaked overnight in a 10 percent chlorine bleach solution, then rinsed thoroughly under hot running water for

Melanotaenia maccullochi, a type 2 egg scatterer, prefers spawning sites in the middle or near the bottom of the spawning tank. This preference is shared by other Australasian rainbowfishes.

several minutes before being used. Sterilize mops in this same way before moving them from one tank to another to avoid the risk of undetected eggs being moved from one tank to another.

Inducing spawning and caring for zygotes: To induce spawning, merely introduce a male and one or two previously conditioned females into the tank in the evening; fish will begin spawning with first light the following morning and will typically be finished by noon. Wait until evening to remove the day's egg production from the spawning mops, as the eggs require a period of contact with water before their shells toughen to the point where they can be safely manipulated.

If a pool of females has been conditioned for the spawning effort, remove the spent female(s) to a separate tank for a few days of reconditioning, and replace with an equivalent number of fresh individuals. If only a single pair or trio is available, retain the adults in the breeding tank and feed them generously with live food. Prepared or frozen foods may not be entirely consumed, and might trigger a bacterial bloom that would considerably depress the number of fertile eggs harvested daily.

When using only a pair or trio of fish, daily egg input will lessen after the first day but should then remain fairly constant as long as individuals are well fed. If the number of viable eggs drops abruptly a week to ten days after the pair is placed in the tank, it may signal excessive bacterial buildup. Change 60 to 75 percent of the water, and replace or resterilize the spawning mops.

Spawn-laden mops should be patted or al-lowed to drip nearly dry. Individual eggs or clusters will stand out like tiny glass beads against the nearly dry, dark-colored strands of the mop. Needle-nosed forceps of the type employed to handle postage stamps are ideal for picking eggs off the mop. Slip the tips of the forceps under the individual egg or cluster, then carefully bring them together and lift upwards to push the egg free from the substratum without exerting lateral pressure. If the egg were to be gripped directly, it might be ruptured in the attempt to pull it free from the mop.

Transfer eggs into a clean plastic or glass 50- to 250-milliliter (about 1 to 8 fluid ounces) hatching container filled with water from the breeding tank. Allow 2.0 milliliters of water per zygote (15 zygotes per fluid ounce) for a safe, conservative stocking rate. The hatching container must have a tight-fitting cover to prevent evaporative water loss and consequent alteration of hardness and pH during development. Adding a bacteriostatic agent to the water is advisable. Dilute a single drop of commercially available acriflavine in ten drops of water, then add just enough of the resulting stock solution to the hatching container to impart a pale yellow color to the water. One treatment is usually all that is necessary.

Do not consolidate more than three days' worth of zygotes in a single container, as there is a tendency towards increased mortality among younger zygotes when the age span is greater than this. Check the containers daily, and remove any opaque or fungus-covered eggs with an eyedropper. Such losses should not exceed 10 percent of the total number of eggs over the entire length of the incubation period. Very high mortali-

A typical annual fish habitat in southeastern Brazil, home to several *Cynolebias* species. Below: As it appears during the rainy season.

The same habitat during the dry season.

ties within the first day or two after spawning typically indicate a high proportion of infertile eggs. This may be due to unfavorable conditions within the spawning tank or to male infertility. A sudden upsurge in losses later on usually signals deteriorating conditions in the hatching container, probably as the cumulative result of overstocking. **Rearing fry:** Most type 2 fry can take *Artemia* nauplii immediately upon hatching. To maximize the likelihood that they will encounter these prey, move the newly mobile young by eyedropper from the hatching container to a rearing tank with its water level one-quarter to one-third of its maximum capacity. As the young grow larger, slowly raise the water level until the tank is completely full.

Type 2 egg-scatterer fry are voracious feeders and typically grow rapidly. They are quite vulnerable to nitrogen-cycle mismanagement. Velvet disease, the malady that wreaks the most havoc among type 2 fry, seems invariably to follow episodes of overfeeding or deviation from the regular pattern of partial water changes in the rearing tank. Prevention is much simpler than cure. If serious losses begin to occur, before beginning treatment, transfer all surviving fry to new quarters with fresh water and a mature sponge filter from an unaffected tank to reduce both the number of pathogens present and a major source of environmental stress.

As fry grow older, afford them more growing room. Killifish in particular should not be crowded if male finnage is to attain its maximum development. Because they hatch over an extended period of time, a batch of type 2 egg-scatterer fry is heterogeneous in size. This invites sibling canni-

A vigorous young pair of *Cynolebias nigripinnis,* a South American diver. Like all annual fishes, this species displays extreme sexual dimorphism.

balism. This problem, most pronounced among killifishes, can be minimized by reducing the disparity between the oldest and youngest fry in the rearing tank by placing similarly sized fry in different tanks. Due to precocious male growth superiority, the smaller individuals in any given batch are likely to be females. Other secondary sexual differences usually begin to develop between eight and twelve weeks after hatching. These fish usually begin spawning between six months and one year after hatching.

Breeding Techniques for Annual Fishes

The reproductive pattern of most annual killifishes is markedly seasonal in nature because the temporary pools in which they live are capable of supporting fishes for a very brief time. These fish, usually thought to pose the ultimate challenge to the amateur fish breeder, are in reality no more difficult to breed than other type 2 egg scatterers, given a little research into their maintenance requirements. A number of approaches are detailed in publications of the American and British killifish associations. The method outlined below mimics the natural cycle of these fishes and requires the least effort to implement.

Choosing and conditioning breeding stock: In view of the short life-span of annual fishes, young individuals must be chosen. Obtain trios rather than pairs, as males should be obliged to divide their attentions to minimize the risk of injury to females.

Annual fishes do best in rather soft, neutral to slightly acidic water, and demand careful attention to environmental cleanliness and proper nitrogen-cycle management. Most live longer and remain reproductively active longer at temperatures under 25 degrees C (77 degrees F). Proficient jumpers, they must be kept in a tightly covered tank.

Sexes must be conditioned separately. Most males fight ferociously in the presence of females, and the females' pattern of ripening a relatively small number of eggs daily leads to uncontrolled spawning if the sexes are housed together.

The fecundity of annual fish is directly influenced by the quantity and quality of their food. Feed at least twice, and preferably three times, each day. A high-protein diet is essential (see under "General Guidelines"). Tubificid worms can safely be included in their diet.

Preparation of the spawning tank: In a securely covered tank of appropriate scale (20 to 60 liters or 5 to 15 gallons), place a mature sponge filter, several floating yarn mops (see under "Breeding Techniques for Type 2 Egg Scatterers Without Diapause") to serve as hiding places for spent females, and a heater if needed.

Furnish the tank with a container filled with loose, waterlogged peat. The net-wrapped peat pellets sold in garden shops for horticultural use can be safely added to the breeding tank without further treatment. A less desirable alternative is to use one of the several brands of fibrous peat marketed for the purpose of acidifying aquarium water. To prevent lowering the pH in the breeding tank to toxic levels, these must be boiled in several gallons of demineralized water in a glass or enameled vessel for at least an hour before being added—a practice that leaves the entire house smelling like a peat bog after a heavy rain! Never use either the peat moss sold in bulk as a soil amendment or whole sphagnum moss as a spawning substratum for these fishes. To do so may have disastrous results.

Empty 1- or 2-liter (1- or 2-quart) plastic ice cream containers make excellent peat containers if weighted down with two or three small rocks. Fill a container no more than half full with the soaked peat pellets or conditioned fibrous peat. The depth is determined by whether the species to be bred is a plower (all of the African annual killifishes; South American *Cynolebias*) or a diver (all other Neotropical annual killifishes). Plowers need only enough depth to bury their eggs in a furrow as they move over the bottom. Divers require peat slightly deeper than the total length of the male in order to bury themselves completely when spawning. Partially cover the container, either by cutting a hole in the plastic lid just large enough to allow the breeding pair to move freely in and out or by covering the top with two strips of glass set far enough apart to provide an access slit.

Spawning and incubation: Once they are placed together in the breeding tank, it rarely takes more than a few minutes for fish to discover the peat container. Annual killifish begin spawning at first light and have usually concluded by noon. Spawning typically is so vigorous that peat is tossed several inches into the water column with each bout.

With smaller species, one can hold a single pair or trio in the breeding tank and feed normally, with partial water changes every two or three days for seven to ten days before the eggs are harvested. The heartier appetites and greater fecundity of the most robust annual species justify removing the fish for heavy reconditioning after two or three days of access to the spawning medium without feeding.

Transfer the peat-filled container from the breeding tank to a kitchen strainer. Gently hand-squeeze or allow peat to drain until, when a handful is gently compressed, the resulting bolus will adhere together for a few moments before beginning to crumble and/or the outer surface is dry to the touch. Do not worry about damaging any eggs present in the peat. The eggs have extraordinarily hard shells and can resist far more pressure than a single human hand can exert unaided upon the medium in which they are embedded.

Place the barely moist peat in a plastic bag and seal it tightly. On the outer face of a second bag, use a quick-drying indelible marker to indicate both the species whose eggs are contained therein and the date when the peat was harvested. Insert the first bag inside the second, and seal it in the same manner. The package can now be stored at ordinary room temperature. Alternatively, the egg-laden peat can be stored in plastic refrigerator containers with tight-fitting lids.

Hatching may be from six weeks to nine months away, depending upon the species, the moisture content of the peat, and the temperature at which it is stored. Examine the stored peat every few weeks; if it appears perceptibly drier, repackage it. Plastic containers with tight-fitting lids can be stacked easily, but their contents are more inclined to lose water, so they must be inspected more frequently.

Hatching eggs and rearing fry: To attempt a hatching, empty the egg-laden peat into a shallow glass container and cover it with water from an established aquarium to a depth of no more than 2.5 centimeters (1 inch). Within an hour's time, the first fry will make their appearance. Whatever fry can be expected from this rehydration will have hatched within six hours. Transfer these fry to a rearing tank, as for other type 2 egg-scatterer fry. A single batch of peat may yield several hundred fry. Make certain that adequate tank space to rear them is available before beginning to hatch them out.

Drain the peat again as described above, and

The bubble nest of the dwarf gourami (*Colisa lalia*) protrudes above the surface and is anchored to the plants beneath: seen from the side (top left) and from below (left). The male diligently holds station beneath the nest (above), alert to the approach of both potential mates and possible egg predators.

replace it in storage for another two to three weeks, then wet it again to provoke further development and ultimate hatching of any resting eggs present. In species with very long incubation periods, the number of such eggs is often quite high and one may need to repeat the wetting process several times.

A package's initial wetting often does not yield a very impressive muster of fry. Failure to obtain a hatch even after two or three rewettings may mean that: 1) few eggs were deposited in the peat; 2) few zygotes survived the developmental interval; or 3) the young fish require additional help in breaking free of their shells. Poke through the moist peat; if few fertile eggs are encountered or most of the eggs are covered with fungus, little can be done. However, if the peat contains substantial numbers of "eyed" eggs, increasing the amount of free carbon dioxide in solution will pop the stubborn eggshells. Sprinkle a few pinches of finely powdered dry food over the surface of the hatching tray, and the collective respiration of the resultant bacterial bloom will provide this. As a quicker alternative, add about 1/2 cup (120 milli-

liters) of room-temperature club soda to the water in the tray.

Annual fry can take *Artemia* nauplii immediately upon hatching. Fed generously and often, they display phenomenally rapid growth rates. Care for them like other type 2 egg scatterers, but stock at a lower density than other egg layer fry.

All of these species exhibit both early male growth superiority and sibling cannibalism. Sort by size as soon as possible. Secondary sex characteristics usually begin to appear by the third week after hatching, and some species make tentative spawning attempts a week later. At this point, separation of the sexes is essential to prevent lethal fighting among young males and to allow proper conditioning of females.

Egg Layers That Practice Parental Care

Many people are surprised to discover that such "primitive" animals as fish are capable of complex

While many male anabantoids grow intolerant of one another with the onset of reproductive activity, few species take this tendency to the extreme evinced by these two male Siamese fighting fish (*Betta splendens*).

The distinctive anabantoid spawning embrace is exemplified by this pair of dwarf gouramis (*Colisa lalia*).

parental behavior. In actuality, such behavior is both widespread and long-standing. Among the aquarium fishes, some thirty families out of sixty-eight have at least some parental representatives. Luckily, this impressive assemblage can be easily subdivided into manageable units.

Breeding Techniques for Bubble-Nest Builders and Other Paternally Custodial Egg Layers

Though not rich in aquarium residents, these reproductive guilds include fish that rank among the most easily bred of all egg layers. The popular aphrophils, or bubble-nest builders, are discussed as a paradigm for this group, followed by a brief supplementary treatment of idiosyncrasies of those species with different spawning site preferences.

Selecting and conditioning breeding stock: Select several vigorous, young, well-colored individuals of each sex as breeding stock, for courtship in these species is variably expressed and one cannot automatically assume that any male and female randomly placed together will prove compatible.

Although many of these species will spawn in a community tank, such spontaneous reproductive efforts rarely produce fry. To increase chances for successful spawning, a more controlled environment must be provided. Begin by conditioning the sexes in separate tanks within sight of one another. Such deliberate arousal tends to make

females more receptive to male advances once the sexes are placed together and almost always triggers the onset of nesting behavior in males. Males of the more aggressive belontiids, such as *Belontia signata* and *Betta splendens,* must each be provided with separate quarters to prevent damaging or even lethal fights.

Feed the intended breeders heavily during the conditioning period, which typically lasts two to three weeks. At least two, and preferably three, feedings a day are essential, of which half should be of live food or high-quality frozen foods such as bloodworms, glassworms, adult brine shrimp, or, where appropriate, small fish. Females will become quite heavy-bodied as their eggs mature.

Preparing the spawning tank: These fish do not require a spotless environment, for the placement of zygotes at the water's surface, combined with the males' hygienic behavior, minimizes the risk of bacterial or fungal attack. A well-established aquarium with a blanket of green algae on its back and sides makes an ideal breeding tank.

It is essential that the tank be large enough to allow the female adequate room to maneuver and that it afford her some possibility of concealment. The two sexes may not be in full reproductive synchrony when first placed together, and males of many of these species will attack sexually unreceptive females vigorously. A layer of floating plants, clumps of bunch plants such as *Anacharis* or *Hygrophila,* inverted flower pots with enlarged drainage holes, or nylon yarn mops (see under "Breeding Techniques for Type 2 Egg Scatterers Without Diapause") increase the female's margin of safety.

The breeding tank also must be large enough to provide adequate growing room for the resulting young. Aphrophil fry are extremely fragile until they fully develop aerial respiration. Attempts to transfer them prior to this point typically result in massive losses. Smaller belontiids require a 60-liter (15-gallon) aquarium; for a spawn of larger fish such as kissing gourami, a 100-liter (25-gallon) breeder flat is barely sufficient.

None of these fish prosper in extremely hard alkaline water, but most are otherwise indifferent to its chemical composition. Fill the tank no deeper than 20 cm (about 8 inches), and insert the thermostatic heater at an angle. A mature sponge filter is the fibration system of choice, but whatever type of filter is employed, regulate its operation to minimize disturbance of the water surface. Air-driven units should pass no more than a single bubble through the return stem each minute. Provide a tightly fitting tank cover; failure to do so invites large-scale fry mortality during the period of transition to aerial respiration. The tank may be brightly lit. These species are either indifferent to the level of illumination or positively stimulated by bright light.

Induction of spawning and management of zygotes: These fish are polygamous under natural conditions, but if fish are set up in multiple female groups in the aquarium, males will usually court one female and attack the others. Females also may squabble seriously with one another. Set these fish up as single pairs. To moderate the tempo of behavioral interaction and reduce the risk that the female will be attacked, move a single pair into the spawning tank just before turning the tank lights off for the night.

Aphrophils typically spawn with the arrival of the rainy season in nature. Spawning appears to follow most swiftly if breeders are introduced to the tank immediately before the arrival of a low-pressure front. It also is sometimes helpful to replace part of the water in the breeding tank with fresh, slightly cooler water of the same chemical makeup.

Monitor the interaction between the male and female carefully. A certain amount of chasing and nipping is not unusual, but persistent harassment, evinced by badly torn fins and missing scales, can lead to the female's death. If such behavior is observed, immediately remove the female. If only a single pair is available, one can separate initially incompatible fish with a glass partition and condition them further until their demeanor suggests readiness to spawn. The main disadvantage of this approach lies in the male's tendency to build his nest immediately adjacent to the partition, which causes the nest to break apart when the barrier is lifted. If one floats the lid from a cup- or pint-sized (250- to 500-milliliter) plastic container near the partition, the male will usually construct his nest beneath it instead.

After a period of reciprocal circling, the couple will move immediately below the nest. The male then arches his body around that of the female, who releases a number of eggs which are immediately fertilized. In those species with buoyant eggs, the zygotes float up into the nest. Otherwise the male will pick them up in his mouth and spit them between the nest's bubbles. Such behavior is repeated until the female is spent, at which point the male will immediately drive her away from the nest so that she cannot devour the eggs. If she cannot hide, she may be killed. Remove her from the tank immediately.

In nature, males drive off egg predators, maintain the integrity of the bubble mass, retrieve eggs that may fall from the nest, and remove (and/or eat) infertile eggs. In the more benign environment of captivity, a male's presence is rarely essential to the survival of the zygotes. Many breeders remove the male almost as soon as spawning is completed. Retaining the male with the bubble nest allows one to witness a suite of complex and fascinating behavior patterns. However, once the fry are fully mobile, the male is apt to eat them if they cannot disperse. Remove him prior to this point.

Rearing of fry: The technique for rearing aprophil fry is in most respects identical to that used for type 1 egg scatterers. Most require infusoria for their first three to seven days of active existence, followed by microworms or the smallest of *Artemia* nauplii. Their appetites are hearty, making the culturing of microscopic food in sufficient quantity a major project in itself. Anabantoid fry are initially lethargic about actively seeking out food; a low water level reduces the volume within which the infusoria can disperse. Once the fry have grown large enough to take nauplii, the water level can be gradually raised.

Fry are extremely susceptible to velvet disease if exposed to the stress of elevated nitrite levels. Partial water changes are essential, but anabantoid fry are very sensitive to both abrupt temperature drops and dissolved chlorine. The transition period between purely branchial respiration and development of the ability to utilize atmospheric oxygen is particularly dangerous. Mortalities can be minimized if the rearing tank is tightly covered and water changes are stopped until all the fry are regularly rising to the surface to gulp air. Chemically active filter media are a useful tool for maintaining water quality during this interval.

The sort of biparental custodial behavior exemplified by this pair of *Heros sajica* is extremely unusual among fishes.

Sort the fry by size as soon as they are capable of atmospheric respiration. If reducing the total number of fry being reared, remember precocious male growth superiority. For maximal growth, stock the fry at the densities recommended for type 2 egg scatterers.

Once secondary sexual characteristics become evident, segregate the young fish by sex. Males of pugnacious species will scrap incessantly and must be reared in isolation for their finnage to develop its full potential.

Modifications for other paternally custodial fishes: The spawning requirements and behavior of the remaining paternally custodial guilds share many similarities with the bubble-nest builders. However, one must carefully research the reproductive idiosyncrasies of a particular species before attempting breeding.

Most of these species are fairly small and require only a 60-liter (15-gallon) tank. In nature they occupy habitats that range from blackwater streams and marshes to brackish lagoons and river estuaries, and most are relatively intolerant of deviations from the conditions that prevail in their native habitat. Replicate such conditions closely when setting up the breeding tank. A combination of extra caves and abundant bunch plants should be added to provide plentiful shelter for the female.

The species to be bred must be furnished with a choice of spawning sites compatible with its reproductive pattern. Cavity spawners respond to clay flower pots cut in half lengthwise or pieces of chlorinated polyvinylchloride (CPVC) pipe of an appropriate diameter. For those species which excavate their own spawning site, bury such structures in the substratum.

For species that utilize a single plant leaf as a spawning site, the various swordplants of the genus *Echinodorus* are particularly convenient because they respond well to potting and thus can be easily moved from one tank to another as needed. Furthermore, their leaves are quite tough, which allows them to stand up to the site-cleaning that is an integral part of the prespawning behavior of these species. Plastic replicas are also well accepted.

Other species that spawn in the open and mouthbrooders require minimal attention with regard to spawning sites. For species that dig a pit, the particle size of tank gravel should be fine enough to be easily manipulated. If the fish spawns upon a solid surface, provide a number of rocks of various shapes, pieces of waterlogged driftwood, or plastic replicas of the foregoing.

Such paternally custodial egg layers as sunfish and darters are cool-water species that require a low-temperature resting period to mature their gonads. The proximate trigger to spawning is usually a simultaneous increase in day length and water temperature. Tropical species, on the other hand, usually respond positively to a tropical rainstorm, simulated by replacement of part of the breeding tank's volume with fresh water a few degrees cooler.

Removing the female immediately after spawning is prudent, although males of most of these species are more tolerant than are male anabantoids. Only when the normal sequence of parental behavior breaks down need the aquarist concern himself with the developing zygotes. In this case, it may be necessary to resort to artificial incubation (see under "Breeding Techniques for Monogamous Cichlids"). Males should be removed as soon as the fry become free-swimming.

Breeding Techniques for Monogamous Cichlids

Monogamy, absolutely correlated with biparental care of the zygotes, is extremely unusual among fishes. The treatment in this section concentrates exclusively upon the family Cichlidae, but the aquarist wishing to spawn other monogamous fishes should find the methods equally relevant.

Most authors divide cichlids into substratum-spawning versus mouthbrooding species. However, the aspect of cichlid reproductive biology most relevant to the aquarist is their mating system, for the presence or absence of a long-term bond between the sexes determines how the fish will be handled before and after spawning.

Monogamous cichlids have an undeserved reputation for being difficult to breed in captivity. They are less flexible in their space requirements than are many other egg-laying fishes, and the complexity of their reproductive behavior demands more concern with the preliminaries to spawning than with subsequent management of the zygotes. The key to breeding them successfully lies in obtaining a compatible pair.

Preparing the spawning tank: Cichlid conditioning and breeding typically take place in the aquarium where the adults are normally maintained. With few exceptions, monogamous cichlids are among the larger ornamental fishes. Sexually active individuals are intensely territorial and extremely fecund. Cichlids in the 8 to 15 centimeter (about 3 to 6 inches) standard length (SL) size range routinely produce spawns of up to 500 fry. Those of larger species can number in the thousands. For all these reasons, adequate living space is of critical importance. I can state categorically that 95 percent of the aquaristically undesirable activity attributed to cichlids results from attempts to keep and breed them in tanks

too small to allow the normal expression of their behavior. Only the so-called dwarf cichlids can be successfully bred in 40- to 60-liter (10- to 15-gallon) tanks. Ideally, most species in the 10 to 15 centimeter (about 4 to 6 inches) SL range should be given a 160-liter (40-gallon) breeder flat. A 200-liter (50-gallon) aquarium represents the bare minimum for larger species, which should really be provided with tanks in the 300-liter to 400-liter (75- to 100-gallon) range.

Cichlids combine hearty appetites with considerable sensitivity to dissolved metabolic wastes. Their tendency to dig vigorously makes under-gravel filters impractical. Sponge or canister filters can be successfully employed with dwarf cichlids and most medium-sized species. Large cichlids require a high-capacity outside power filter. Adherence to a routine of frequent partial water changes is essential. Outfit the tank with a sealed-unit thermostatic heater and a close-fitting cover.

Cichlids are very sensitive to overhead motion. They do best in tanks positioned at roughly chest level or higher. They appear more at ease under a cover of floating plants and with a gravel layer to eliminate light reflection from the tank bottom. The tank must be well furnished with both cover and potential breeding sites.

Determine the spawning site preference of a given species before setting up its quarters. Some, such as angelfish and discus, do well in densely vegetated habitats. Many of the family's medium-sized or larger members will destroy plants and require alternate furnishings such as rockwork, driftwood, clay flower pots, or sections of CPVC pipe. The foundations of any rockwork must be placed solidly on the tank bottom rather than on the gravel surface, where the fish will undermine them.

Management of pair formation: Four methods are commonly used. The first requires a much larger tank than the other three methods.

1. The Naturalistic Method. In nature, a cichlid pair has many suitable targets against which to redirect their aggressive behavior. As long as these intruders can move beyond the boundaries of a defended area, they run minimal risk of injury. Kept as a single pair in captivity, cichlids often turn upon one another.

If six to eight young conspecifics are raised to maturity together in a large enough tank, the first pair to form will exclude the remaining fish from a portion of it and settle down to breeding. A single male and female will also pair readily and spawn freely if kept in a community of behaviorally compatible heterospecifics.

2. The Target Fish Method. A potential spawn predator need not be physically accessible to a cichlid pair to discharge its stabilizing function. Isolated by a clear partition, it will be attacked with the same fury as if it were physically accessible. Thus, one can partition off a portion of the breeding tank and place a solitary specimen of any comparably sized cichlid in it, out of reach of the breeding pair. A more efficient approach, however, is to place a breeding pair on either side of the partition. A piece of plastic egg crate diffuser grating works well. If glass is used instead, a filter must operate in each compartment and the glass must be kept clean. If the target fish cannot be clearly seen by the pair, the spawning effort may fail and the female may be killed by the males.

3. The Privileged Sanctuary Method. Males of most monogamous cichlids grow a good deal larger than do females. Divide the breeding tank with a barrier with several openings which allow the female free movement from one side to the other while confining the male to a single larger compartment that includes the future spawning site, which should be placed as close to the barrier as possible. This approach allows the pair to interact directly with minimal risk, for the female can move out of the male's reach should his attentions become overbearing or dangerous.

4. The Incomplete Divider Method. In sight of one another, a male and female often will perform their respective parts of the spawning act even when physically separated. Either plastic diffuser grating or a glass barrier raised slightly from the tank bottom near the spawning site will allow enough of the male's sperm to diffuse through to fertilize some fraction of the egg plaque. This method protects the female, yet because it allows fry to move freely between the two compartments it allows both sexes to assume a parental role. Its disadvantages are that it totally eliminates normal behavioral interactions between the adults and that many of the female's eggs will not be fertilized. Breeders often use this method for single pairs of very large cichlids that are so aggressive and fecund that it seems desirable to trade off a percentage of the spawn to guarantee the safety of hard-to-replace breeding stock.

Postspawning management: Pairs will usually

The exclusively female brood care shown by this female *Apistogramma agassizi* is a prerequisite for the evolution of both harem polygyny and open polygamy in cichlids.

signal their intent to spawn by a sudden increase in the frequency of pit digging and nipping off of the future spawning site. Spawning can be expected within twenty-four hours of the appearance of the female's ovipositor, a conspicuous blunt-tipped tube that protrudes from her vent.

Postspawning behavior normally includes well-developed and highly efficient custodial and hygienic elements. Occasionally, this care breaks down, resulting in parental cannibalism. Faced with this situation, one should remove the zygotes from the breeding tank and hatch them artificially. Such episodes are typical of young pairs and usually cease once the fish have grown older.

Artificial rearing: Artificial hatching of cichlid eggs must be regarded as a method of last resort, for no matter how carefully the spawn is handled, a significant percentage of the resulting fry will be congenitally deformed. Remove the egg plaque to a 2- to 5-gallon (about 8- to 20-liter) aquarium with fresh water of the same temperature and chemical makeup as that in the breeding tank. Place an airstone next to the plaque and bleed a gentle stream of air into the tank to create a gentle current that mimics the fanning behavior of the female. Zygotes of cave-spawning cichlids are markedly light-sensitive. Cover their tank with brown wrapping paper until the fry are fully mobile.

Add a bacteriostatic agent to the hatching tank. Neutral acriflavine used at half the recommended medicinal dosage or MarOxy used at the manufacturer's recommended dosage are more effective than methylene blue, the traditional choice.

After hatching, fry should be housed in such a hatching tank for no more than a few days. During this period, slowly replace the original medicated water with fresh water from the tank to which they will ultimately be transferred. To move the fry, carefully siphon off all but 1 or 2 liters or quarts of the hatching tank's volume, then pour the remaining water and fry into the rearing tank. This is far safer than netting them.

Most fry (and their parents!) will take *Artemia* nauplii and finely powdered prepared foods; the few very small species can manage microworms. Cichlid fry should be fed at least two or preferably three or four times daily. The schedule of partial water changes in the breeding tank should reflect their voracious feeding habits.

In nature, custodial care persists until the fry no longer respond to parental efforts to control their movements (six to eight weeks in most species). Brood protection effectively precludes normal foraging behavior, so the female does not yolk up a second batch of eggs during this time. In captivity, a female may mature another clutch of eggs and attempt another spawning well before the fry are fully independent. Separate parents and offspring as soon as the pair shows persistent signs of respawning. Their behavior toward their older progeny at this point varies from indifference to active hostility.

Cichlid fry grow rapidly but unevenly. If not sorted by size, they will usually cull one another quite efficiently. Because they are characterized by precocious male growth superiority, the end result will be a strongly male-biased sex ratio among the hardy survivors. It is rarely in one's best interest to try rearing an entire brood of one of these more prolific species. The optimal course of action is to randomly net out a few hundred fry for future rearing when separating them from their parents, and use the remainder as a source of live food for other large fish. This course of action duplicates the eventual fate of nine out of every ten cichlid fry in nature.

Breeding Techniques for Polygamous Cichlids (Harem Holders and Maternal Mouthbrooders)

For many decades, virtually the only cichlids available to aquarists were characterized by a monogamous mating system. However, many cichlids with maternal care have a mating system in which one or both sexes interact with multiple spawning partners during the duration of a single reproductive period. In harem polygyny, a single male controls access to and spawns with the same group of females over an extended period. In open polygamy, the association between the sexes is restricted to the sexual act itself and both male and female may have multiple partners during a single spawning effort; these latter cichlids all practice maternal mouthbrooding. This group includes the popular mbuna and peacock cichlids from Lake Malawi.

Management of polygynous harem holders: Most of these cichlids are dwarf species, but females expand their territories after spawning has occurred. If the tank is too small, the male, even if bigger than the female, runs risk of serious injury or even death after spawning is complete. Aquaria in the 60- to 80-liter (15- to 20-gallon) range will comfortably and safely house a single male and two or three females of most of these species. More than a single male may be housed in the same tank only if each has sufficient space to stake out his own domain. The non-dwarf species, of course, require considerably larger quarters.

Dwarf representatives of this group are given to hiding for extensive periods when housed alone. To help eliminate this shyness and elicit a more reliable manifestation of female parental behavior, add six to twelve smaller schooling fish. The behavior of such "dither fish" serves to reassure the cichlids that their immediate environment is danger-free. Choose a species that will neither outcompete the cichlids at feeding time nor pose a significant threat to mobile cichlid fry. Do not use catfish or loaches, as they pose a threat to cichlid fry and are often attacked or killed by the adults before spawning.

Except for the robust *Acarichthys* and *Guianacara* species, these fish are tolerant of aquatic plants and appear to do better in heavily planted aquaria. Overall, their maintenance requirements are identical to those of their monogamous relatives. Females are usually reliable and efficient parents, but young mothers may devour their first few clutches. Eggs can be artificially incubated following the procedure outlined for monogamous cichlids.

Parental care usually persists for three to four weeks in captivity. As she begins to ripen a new batch of eggs, the female loses interest in, then drives away, her older progeny. Remove them for rearing elsewhere. Fry can be fed and managed in the same way as monogamous cichlid fry. All are extremely sensitive to dissolved metabolic wastes, so regular partial water changes are essential. Sibling cannibalism is not prevalent among most of these cichlids.

Prespawning management of openly polygamous cichlids: No openly polygamous mating system is characterized by the long-term association of a male and female. Virtually all failures with these fish stem from the mistaken belief that they can be maintained as isolated single pairs. The inevitable consequence of such efforts is a badly battered or dead female.

The smallest tanks within which most of these fish can be safely housed is 200 liters (50 gallons); tanks in the 300- to 360-liter (75- to 95-gallon) range are far better. Larger species require even more room.

Two approaches are equally effective in protecting individual females from continuous male harassment. The simplest maintains the fish as single pairs in a rather crowded community tank of behaviorally and environmentally compatible cichlids. Most amateur breeders are partial to this approach because it allows them to maintain a wider variety of species in the space at their disposal. The second is to maintain openly polygamous cichlids by themselves in single male–multiple female groups so that the sheer number of potential spawning partners keeps a male from concentrating on one female long enough to injure or kill her. A ratio of three females to one male seems to be the lower limit. Commercial breeders are partial to this approach because it maximizes output of fry while eliminating all possibility of accidental hybridization.

The maintenance requirements of openly polygamous cichlids are otherwise similar to those of their monogamous counterparts. All have hearty appetites and fortunately are not fussy eaters.

Postspawning management of openly polygamous cichlids: These cichlids spawn freely in either a mixed-species community or when housed in single-species "harems." Among most of these species, the female picks up her eggs immediately after depositing them and fertilization subsequently takes place inside her buccal cavity. In nature, after spawning, the female seeks out a sheltered spot well away from the breeding site. When essentially herbivorous species, such as the mbuna, are maintained as single-species breeding groups in reasonably well-furnished tanks and fed well, a purely naturalistic approach is quite feasible, for fry run little risk of predation. In most cases, however, survival in a mixed-species community is a chancy proposition, and a parental female comes in for a good deal more harassment than she would be likely to encounter either in nature or in a single-species breeding group.

For at least the first three and preferably seven days, keep the ovigerous female in the breeding tank with ample cover. Attempts to move her any earlier may cause her to prematurely spit out the progeny permanently. Then move her to a nursery tank of 20 liters (5 gallons) or more, depending upon her size. Never house more than one female per tank. If using several compartments, separate the fish with an opaque partition. If ovigerous females can see one another, they may become so disturbed that they will expel or devour their broods.

Many females maintain a light intake of food during the incubation period, but it is not essential to offer food. Replace part of the water in the tank every three to five days until the young become mobile. Metabolic functions do not cease simply because a fish is not eating, and developing zygotes also generate a significant amount of metabolic waste.

If faced with the need to artificially rear the zygotes of these advanced mouthbrooding cichlids as an emergency measure, one can find many published workable designs for an "artificial mouth." All have some arrangement for gently circulating water in a small container to imitate the tumbling which developing young are given in their mother's buccal cavity. Bacteriostatic preparations should be used as suggested for artificial hatching of other cichlid eggs, but at a lower concentration. Partially change the water every other day, adding sufficient medication to replace the amount lost in this process. Mortalities are inevitable, even with the best of care. Check the vessel frequently and remove any dead young before their decomposition fouls the water, leading in turn to further losses.

The duration of buccal incubation varies between species and is also influenced by ambient temperature. In nature, the female seeks out a secluded area to release her fry. In captivity, females are often reluctant to release their offspring in the bare surroundings of a nursery tank, or may be so ill at ease that they will pick them up again at the slightest disturbance. Once the fry have become free-swimming, it is a relatively simple matter to remove them from the buccal cavity of females 7.5 to 10.0 centimeters (about 3 to 4 inches) SL and larger. Hold the female within the folds of a net, head down over a container filled with water from the nursery tank. Gently pull open her lower jaw and immerse her head in the container. The young will usually swim out. Gentle shaking may be required to dislodge the last few.

Smaller species should be handled somewhat differently. Insert the female head down in an ordinary kitchen baster from which the squeeze bulb has been removed. Replace the bulb, then insert the tip of the baster into a container filled with water from the nursery tank. Squeezing the bulb gently several times will force water back and forth through the female's buccal cavity and flush the fry into the receiving container. If several minutes of squeezing produce no effect, remove the baster from the water. Hold it, opening down, over the container for a few moments, then reimmerse it and repeat the cycle of flushing. Fry should begin to emerge from the opening of the baster after a few squeezes.

Some breeders advocate a period of reconditioning for the female prior to her reintroduction to the society of other fishes. This is not essential provided the dominance in her tank of origin is disrupted somewhat by a partial water change coupled with a rearrangement of the tank furnishings.

Fry of these cichlids are robust and may be handled in the same manner as substratum-spawning cichlids. Stock at the same densities recommended for live-bearers. Most grow rapidly, even by cichlid standards.

Selected References

Balon, E. K. 1975. Ecological guilds of fishes: a short summary of the concept and its applications. *Verh. Internat. Verien. Limnol.* 19: 2430–39. (The grouping of aquarium fish by reproductive pattern employed in this chapter was based upon Balon's concept of spawning guilds. Recommended reading for all serious fish culturists.)

Emmens, C. W. 1953. *Keeping and Breeding Aquarium Fishes.* New York: Academic Press. (Many useful suggestions on setting up a large-scale breeding effort, choosing and conditioning brood stock, and rearing fry. No longer in print, but copies often can be found in second-hand book shops specializing in scientific and technical titles.)

Goldstein, R. J. 1973. *Cichlids of the World.* Neptune City, N.J.: T.F.H. Publications. (Helpful suggestions on the artificial hatching of cichlid eggs and the management of cichlid fry.)

Innes, W. T. 1959. *Exotic Aquarium Fishes.* Philadelphia: Innes Publications. (The most useful manual of aquarium husbandry to date published in English. Suggests approaches to spawning most of the major groups of ornamental fishes. The section dealing with live foods and their culture is particularly helpful.)

Jocher, W. 1972. *Spawning Problem Fishes.* Books I and II. Neptune City, N.J.: T.F.H. Publications. (An excellent English translation of a two-part German work. "Recipes" for spawning a selection of the more challenging aquarium fishes. Heavy emphasis upon type 1 egg scatterers native to blackwater habitats.)

Loiselle, P. V. 1985. *The Cichlid Aquarium.* Tetra Press. (The most current and comprehensive English language reference on the husbandry of the major biparentally custodial and maternally parental aquarium fishes.)

Mayland, H. J. 1978. *Cichliden und Fischzucht.* Hannover, Ger.: Landbuch-Verlag. (Text is in German. Superb color photographs of the reproductive behavior of a wide variety of aquarium fishes.)

Pinter, H. 1986. *Labyrinth Fish.* New York: Barron's Educational Series. (The most current general reference on the aquarium husbandry of the major aphrophil aquarium fishes.)

Socolof, R. B. 1980. Tropicals. In *Fish Farming Handbook,* ed. E. A. Brown and J. B. Gratzek, 163–205. Westport, Conn.: Avi Publishing Co. (Detailed account of methods employed to produce tropical fish on a commercial scale.)

Wickler, W. 1973. *Breeding Behavior of Aquarium Fishes.* Revised English language edition. Neptune City, N.J.: T.F.H. Publications. (Valuable overview of the reproductive biology of aquarium fishes from the perspective of an internationally recognized authority on fish behavior.)

Contributors

JOHN GRATZEK received a bachelor of science degree in biology and chemistry at St. Mary's College in Minnesota, where he studied the parasites of muskrats. Pursuing his interests in animal disease, he was awarded the Doctor of Veterinary Medicine degree from the University of Minnesota in 1956 and a Ph.D. in the study of animal virology from the University of Wisconsin in 1961. Dr. Gratzek presently heads the Department of Medical Microbiology in the College of Veterinary Medicine at the University of Georgia. He is past president of the American College of Veterinary Microbiologists and the International Association for Aquatic Animal Medicine, and serves on the aquaculture committee of the American Association of Animal Health.

PAUL V. LOISELLE received his master of science degree from Occidental College in Los Angeles and Ph.D. from the University of California at Berkeley. An accomplished aquarist with over twenty years of experience, Dr. Loiselle has served as a consultant for the ornamental fish farming industry in Florida and is currently curator of freshwater fish at the New York Aquarium. He is the author of *The Cichlid Aquarium*, coauthor of the *Marine Aquarist Manual*, and coeditor of *Aquarium Digest International*. His experience in the pond culture of fishes began during five years of Peace Corps service in West Africa.

JOANNE NORTON received bachelor of science, master of science, and Ph.D. degrees in botany from Ohio State University. She began raising tropical fish in 1958. Working in her home, she has investigated the genetics of live-bearers and has developed and introduced to the hobby a number of new fish. In freshwater angelfish, she discovered the inheritance of pigment-pattern genes and pearlscale. After finding that photoperiod influences the expression of several angelfish pigment-pattern genes, Dr. Norton determined the genotypes and day lengths required to produce certain color patterns. She has published two booklets, one on platys and the other on platys and swordtails, written 70 articles, and edited *Livebearers* for its first eight years. She is continuing to work on angelfish genetics and on attempts to improve and develop new mollies.

Index of Scientific Names

Subject Index